WHAT OTHERS SAY ABOUT THIS BOOK...

Most chronic diseases are due to our behavior: hard time changing their diet and lifestyle. In eloquently describes how the support of our lou critically-important difference. This book is a passionate call to action, and I highly recommend it.

—Dean Ornish, M.D., Founder and President, Preventive Medicine Research Institute, Clinical Professor of Medicine, University of California, San Francisco, and Author, *Love & Survival* and *Dr. Dean Ornish's Program for Reversing Heart Disease.*

The peer support approach was very helpful at Union Pacific Railroad. Too often health improvement programs neglect the team and focus exclusively on individual change. Teamwork is central to other successful business practices. Not Alone applies this fundamental business strategy toward creating healthier corporate culture and healthier employees.

— Joe Leutzinger, Ph.D., Principal, Health Improvement Solutions and former Director of Health Promotion, Union Pacific Railroad

This groundbreaking book continues the Allen family tradition of addressing the need for cultural support to achieve wellness. Dr. Allen, like his father, the late Dr. Robert Allen, offers a unique and much needed perspective on how we can work together to bring about lasting and positive change.

— Don Ardell, Ph.D., Editor, *The Ardell Wellness Report*

Not Alone *shows us how support from others is key to successful behavior change. It is practically impossible to adopt and maintain healthy behaviors without it.*

— Steven Aldana, Ph.D., Author, *The Culprit & The Cure* and *The Stop & Go Fast Food Nutrition Guide*

Not Alone *is a comprehensive resource for health promotion practitioners seeking to build a foundation for cultural change. A 'must have' to provide optimal behavior change interventions and support.*

— Erica Wandtke, M.A., National Health Promotion Coordinator, U.S. Department of Health and Human Services

NOT ALONE

Healthy Habits, Helpful Friends

Judd Allen, Ph.D.

President, Human Resources Institute, LLC

Published by

healthyculture.com

Burlington, Vermont

Contact information:

Human Resources Institute, LLC

151 Dunder Road

Burlington, VT 05401 USA

(802) 862-8855

Info@healthyculture.com

www.Healthyculture.com

Quantity purchases of *Not Alone* are available for educational, business and community use.

Cartoon drawings by Isabella Bannerman. Ms. Bannerman also works on a newspaper comic strip, syndicated by King Features, called "Six Chix." More information is available at Isabellabannerman.com.

Cover photographs available through Getty Images. The people shown are models used for illustrative purposes only.

Contents

Acknowledgments

I would like to thank my friends, family, colleagues and clients for their input and enthusiasm.

My father, Robert Allen, Ph.D., inspired my interest in supportive cultural environments and wellness. This book is a tribute to his life's work. Until his death, he was my personal and professional mentor.

Other family members also provided emotional support for my writing efforts. Among them are Anne, Morgan, Peter, Rhonda, Matthew and Robert Allen as well as Elaine and Bob Smith, Mary and Marvin Sochet.

I'm grateful to my wellness buddies Rick Blount, Jonathan Sands, Rick Hubbard, Emina Burak, Fred Cohen, Jim Carmen, James Dingley, Clay Warren and Betsy Baker. These friends have shown me the power of peer support in my own life.

Jack Travis, Meryn Callander, Joe Leutzinger, David Hunnicutt, Feyedra Matthes and Gabe Cohen offered great editorial assistance.

Thanks to my colleagues Troy Adams, Steve Aldana, Don Ardell, Bill Baun, Craig Becker, Larry Chapman, Dee Edington, Dennis Elsenrath, David Gobble, Ken Holtyn, Bill Hettler, Michael O'Donnell, Ahnna Lake, Gillian Pieper, Kay Ryan and Elaine Sullivan. These wellness experts have been particularly helpful in making sure my work is both based in good science and is practical.

Thanks also to the National Wellness Institute, Wellness Councils of America, Health Improvement Solutions, the Institute for Health and Productivity Management and the *American Journal of Health Promotion* as well as the many businesses, communities and organizations that have embraced and tested the Wellness Mentoring concepts.

About the Author

Judd Allen earned his Ph.D. in Community Psychology from New York University. He is President of the Human Resources Institute (also known as Healthyculture.com), a research, publishing and consulting firm that focuses on the creation of supportive cultural environments. Dr. Allen serves on the editorial board of the *American Journal of Health Promotion* and is on the Board of Directors of the National Wellness Institute and a trustee of Perhaps Kids Meeting Kids Will Make a Difference. He has taught on the faculties of Nebraska Methodist College, Cornell University Medical College, Johnson State College and the Institute for Health and Productivity Management. Dr. Allen teaches four online courses: Wellness Mentoring, Wellness Leadership, Culture Change and Creating a Health Work Climate. He has held the position of Senior Research Analyst at Memorial Sloan-Kettering Cancer Center and served on the Vermont Governor's Council for Physical Fitness and Sports.

He loves to travel, exercise and play with friends and family. Dr. Allen has completed more than 20 consecutive New York City Marathons, multiple Ironman™ distance triathlons and long distance cross-country ski races. He lives in Burlington, Vermont, with his wife and daughter.

A Call to Action

Not alone...

- Because lifestyle changes rarely sticks without supportive peers (such as housemates, family, friends and coworkers). You and your peers don't have the patience, energy and time for failure.

- Because giving and getting peer support is one of the healthiest things you can do.

- Because it is more fun and less painful to change with others.

- Because almost all of us attempt to achieve healthier habits. We're in this together.

The Wellness Behavior Change Challenge

When it comes to trying to achieve healthier habits, no one should feel alone. Each year approximately 80 percent of the adults in North America attempt to lose weight, manage stress, become more physically active, stop smoking or change another daily behavior.

Our wellness stories unfold everyday and touch all of us. As a result, you've probably heard a wellness story similar to the following.

- Two days of resolve toward weight loss and now a pint of ice cream. After eating the ice cream, Carmen felt that all hope was lost. She wanted the fat to disappear, but just couldn't keep herself on track.

- Jim knew that his wife, Linda, was going to be angry. This was the third day this week he had stopped by the bar after work. He had promised Linda he'd quit drinking. Alcohol really was making his life miserable, but maybe he hadn't hit bottom yet.

- The phone rang and it was another creditor. Jack knew these credit cards were a trap. He thought to himself, "How could I be so stupid? I've been here before. I'm making good money. Why can't I live within my budget?"

- Dr. Larch felt helpless. This was the second child with diabetes he had diagnosed this week, and he couldn't understand why. Pediatricians aren't supposed to treat type 2 diabetes. Weren't these kids supposed to be eating their vegetables and riding their bikes? Dr. Larch hoped that his lifestyle advice to parents would sink in, but he could see that they too were out of shape.

- Al kept nodding off. He nearly drove off the road, but was able to pull the big truck off the shoulder and back into the lane. These night hours were murder. The company seminar had warned him of the dangers of sleep deprivation. If only he could get some sleep when off work during the daytime.

- Jane hoped the new health promotion program would meet the needs of her aging workforce and control medical costs. As director of human resources she understood that employees were counting on getting medical insurance. Still, this year's premium increase would erase all hope for a profit. The CEO and shareholders will not be happy with her report.

- Governor Smith wanted to be known as fiscally conservative, but with the rise in state employee insurance, Medicaid and Medicare costs were going to cause real pain by forcing cuts in discretionary funding. Still, he believed a tax increase was out of the question. Something had to give. A statewide health promotion program was an option, but Governor Smith was unsure about an effective strategy.

- Rosita was pleased with her husband Juan's medical report. The cardiac rehabilitation was going smoothly. The doctor said that, now after the second heart attack, Juan would really have to eat healthier and get into shape. A heart attack should be a wake-up call, but the last time Juan just couldn't shake his bad habits. This time would be different, or so Rosita hoped.

Each of these stories is both unique and similar. The combination of goals and motivation tend to be unique to the individual. A common thread is that everyone has goals that depend upon lasting and positive behavior change. It is nearly universally true that eliminating unhealthy habits has both individual and societal benefits. Another common thread is that changing unhealthy habits tends to be difficult. In most cases effective peer support would dramatically increase the likelihood of success. The best support must be tailored to individual circumstances.

Lifestyle change attempts are motivated by a wide range of wellness goals including the desire to prevent illness, heal, improve performance and achieve a better quality of life. The desire for self-improvement and self-preservation as well as readily available information about the benefits of healthy practices appear to be making wellness-related behavior change attempts a common phenomenon. Such change efforts are essential to our own wellness and for the health and well being of those we care deeply about.

The fact that we are attempting health behavior changes is great wellness news. Motivation is essential to success, and we appear well motivated to address life-threatening and otherwise unsatisfactory aspects of our day-to-day behavior.

Unfortunately, less than a quarter of these change efforts achieve their behavior change goals. And, most people are trying to make these difficult changes without sufficient support from housemates, family, friends, coworkers and neighbors.

Finally. A home exercise system that really is a clothes rack!

Many of us are trying to change unhealthy habits, but few of these attempts result in lasting behavior change. Maybe you too have exercise equipment that gathers more dust than sweat. Just one in five people who attempt to change behavior actually are successful. After temporary improvements, most of us revert back to prior unhealthy behavior.

We may laugh about the fate of last year's health resolutions, but the toll in terms of higher stress, lower self-esteem, ill health and a sense of helplessness is staggering. Failure to lose weight results in yo-yo dieting, which puts a tremendous strain on the body's metabolism. Similarly, the lack of successful stress management leaves us on edge and predisposed for heart attacks and relationship problems.

Another consequence of failed lifestyle change is increased desperation. Those who have failed are more susceptible to trying less healthy, expensive and more drastic remedies such as stomach reduction surgery and cholesterol reducing drugs.

High failure rates also undermine the efforts of health professionals. Those in a position to offer medical advice are reluctant to do so because they have seen how often patients fail. It's easier to treat the symptom and ignore the behavior that underlies it. High failure rates and their adverse consequences have led many to believe that it is hurtful to advocate behavior change.

Contrary to popular myth, most failures are not due to a lack of motivation, unrealistic goals or personal follow-through. **The primary reason 80 percent of attempted behavior changes fail is a lack of effective support.** People are somehow expected to develop the willpower to adopt healthy behaviors that are contrary to normal practice in their social environments. Too little attention is given to the importance of support factors such as the physical, emotional and social environment.

Friends, family and coworkers are rarely fully engaged in providing support. Behavior change is seen as a private concern. Significant others may be informed about goals, but little thought is given to the support a social network can offer. The emphasis on personal motivation leads to a lot of behavior change attempts, but motivation is rarely adequate to bring about lasting results. *Not Alone* was written to assist you and your peers to achieve wellness goals and to break the cycle of behavior change failure.

Many Try to Change Without Adequate Support

Have you attempted one or more health-related behavior changes during the past year?

If so, how successful were you in achieving your goal or goals?

In 1983, I included these two questions in a study of just over 300 people waiting for their flights at New Jersey's Newark International Airport. Since this preliminary research, I have included these questions (or very similar ones) in more than 100 subsequent research projects in a wide range of community and business settings. The answers to these questions have always been very similar. Approximately 80 percent of those completing the anonymous surveys report having attempted at least one behavior change, but less than 20 percent report success.

Why do so few succeed? What secret ingredient leads to successful change? It turns out that support is the key. The level and quality of support is highly related to lasting behavior change. Without support at work, at home and in the community, people may attempt change, but are unable to maintain their new desired practices.

The positive role of peer support in behavior change has also been a focus of my research in workplaces. The Lifegain Health Culture Audit has been used in several hundred business, health care and educational settings to evaluate and plan wellness programs. Survey results show that when most employees attempt behavior change, they experience low to moderate levels of peer support from family, friends, managers and coworkers. When peer support is enhanced via support groups and other wellness programs, behavior change success rates rise.

I have found repeatedly that improving peer support is an important tool in creating a corporate culture that supports healthy behavior. Such support influences whether people attempt change and their prospects for success. This is the bottom-line issue for a wellness program. Cost savings and productivity improvements never materialize unless behavior changes.

Why Culture is Overlooked

In American culture there is an overemphasis on personal drive, self-motivation, a positive attitude and other personal psychological factors. People are somehow expected to develop the willpower to adopt healthy behaviors that are contrary to normal practice in their social environments. Too little attention is given to the importance of support factors such as the physical, emotional and social environment.

It is not normal in American society to provide support for wellness goals. Such goals are supposed to be accomplished on one's own. Americans live in a culture focused on self-improvement. Let's put this into historical perspective.

The drive for self-improvement dates back to the advent of participatory democracies in such places as ancient Greece about 4,000 years ago. At that time, the relative role and the nature of humans began to be redefined, so that the individual became more important than the clan, family or group. This movement remained relatively small for millennia but gained momentum in the early 1500s with the emergence of the Renaissance in Europe. It was the beginning of a shift in the definition of a person from being a member of a tribe or group to being a unique individual with specific social responsibilities.

With the Reformation, the belief emerged that an individual no longer needed the intercession of the church to have a relationship with God. The emphasis turned to an individual's personal religious experience. Migration to America either as a colonist or as a slave further broke traditional clan and family bonds. Individualism became a part of patriotic folklore, as evident in the *Autobiography of Benjamin Franklin,* tales of Davy Crockett and the *Adventures of Huckleberry Finn.* Western psychology defined mental health in terms of an individual's capacity for self-change. The very idea that someone was dependent on another person was an indication of mental illness.

Our individualistic-centered culture has had an adverse impact on peer support for wellness goals. Many people are unaware that coworkers, family and friends can play a constructive role. And many of us are reluctant to ask for assistance because we do not want to appear weak or inadequate.

In addition, many of us are reluctant to offer assistance because we are unsure just how to proceed and don't want to inadvertently undermine or offend our peers. These usual barriers to giving and receiving help are occasionally overcome when frustration with unsuccessful lifestyle change becomes intolerable or when chronic illnesses and medical emergencies demand drastic intervention.

Effective peer support need not be the last option reserved for emergencies and times of desperation. The culture needs to change to support **both self-determination and mutual support**. *Not Alone* offers tools to raise awareness about the potential for providing support. I want to empower you to give and get effective support useful for achieving lasting behavior change. I believe peer support should become the norm.

Note: As might be expected in a culture that focuses almost exclusively on self-determination, words for peer support may at first sound awkward and unfamiliar. A glossary is available at the end of the book. For the purpose of language clarity in *Not Alone*, the person offering support is called the *mentor* or *Wellness Mentor.*® The person receiving support is the *changer*. In addition, I've alternated between both genders throughout the book rather than referring to a person as him/her or he/she.

First Encounters with Wellness and Support

I first heard the word *wellness* at Frost Valley, the YMCA's largest summer camp, located in the Catskill Mountains of New York State. It was 1978 and I was looking for a job during my high school summer vacation. My father, Robert Allen, Ph.D., had been invited to help teach camp counselors about wellness and suggested that I take a summer job at the camp.

Don Ardell, Ph.D., Bill Hettler, M.D., and John Travis, M.D. (an editor of this book), joined my dad in explaining the wellness concept and how we were to promote wellness among our young summer campers. These guys said that wellness was about good social relationships, managing stress, exercising and eating nutritious foods. We were told that a wellness lifestyle would increase the likelihood of a long and illness-free life. After a week of training, the counselors were enthusiastic about the new wellness initiative.

Everything seemed perfect until the kids started arriving. Their camp trunks were packed with what appeared to be a lifetime supply of junk food and candy. Furthermore, many of the kids had been shipped off to camp because their parents had given up on them and each other. Broken families and psychological problems were commonplace. Wellness didn't look like it was going to come naturally to our campers. They were not thrilled when we described the new camp menu and philosophy.

At our first counselor meeting, we talked about our dilemma. Most counselors complained about the inadequacy of our training. Some questioned whether wellness was such a great idea for our camp. It was clear to many of us that success would only be achieved through addressing peer cultures. Wellness would have to become the new and fun way "we do things around here." We would need to change support systems so that they would promote wellness.

It took some doing, but I'm pleased to report that Frost Valley

YMCA was largely successful. We introduced new health-oriented cooking ideas at "The Incredible Edible House" – a converted maple sugaring shack that now made nutritious alternative treats for the campers. We also developed a wellness manual with over 100 activities designed to introduce various wellness concepts. We incorporated environmental education – a camp strength – into the overall wellness initiative. We revamped chapel services so that kids and counselors could talk about sources of meaning and purpose in life. We introduced yoga postures at our morning camp-wide gathering at the flag pole. We helped each other get the most out of our camp experience and the wellness philosophy. Although we did not call it such, our friendships were based on peer support.

It's been more than 25 years since my introduction to wellness at Frost Valley. Since that time, I have learned a great deal about wellness and the need to empower people to offer effective support. In graduate school I studied the strong relationship between successful behavior change and support. During my first job as a Senior Research Analyst at Memorial Sloan-Kettering Cancer Center, we worked to change peer support systems related to teenage smoking and mammography utilization among Harlem women.

Since becoming President of the Human Resources Institute in 1987, I have had the good fortune to assist hundreds of companies and government agencies in their efforts to support wellness. *Not Alone* draws on a rich and heroic history of people coming together to help one another.

A More Powerful Form of Peer Support

Effective support requires a more organized approach than is typically provided by peers (whether that's a coworker, spouse, housemate, friend, neighbor or another member of a rehabilitation, health or wellness program). Widely used peer support strategies such as listening and offering words of encouragement are only the tip of the iceberg.

More than 25 years of experience leads me to believe that while kindness, compassion, good listening and understanding will be at the heart of effective support, these qualities must be joined with strategic planning and follow-through. Behavior change is very challenging, and it requires a full range of emotional and physical assistance.

The term *Wellness Mentoring*® is used to identify a specific form of helping that is apart from what is typically known as peer support. Wellness Mentoring is a highly organized and comprehensive kind of assistance offered by family, housemates, friends, or coworkers specifically to assist with lasting lifestyle change. The focus of Wellness Mentoring is on empowerment. Wellness Mentoring utilizes a process that establishes a foundation of mutual trust and an agreement for an ongoing conversation about supporting change efforts.

The conversations that are part of Wellness Mentoring sessions include subjects that have been the focus of extensive behavioral science research. For example, Wellness Mentoring sessions incorporate approaches that are central to Albert Bandura's Social Learning Theory and James Prochaska's Transtheoretical Model of Stages of Behavior Change. Bandura's work emphasizes the importance of good role modeling. Prochaska's work focuses on understanding how successful lifestyle change tends to proceed through a number of stages. Lessons gleaned from this behavior change research are incorporated into the Wellness Mentoring strategies offered throughout *Not Alone*.

The Wellness Mentoring approach dramatically enhances our capacity to both get and give needed assistance with behavior change. This assistance offers the power to achieve lasting and positive change without compromising personal integrity and freedom. *Not Alone* was written for anyone seeking to achieve a wellness goal (this person is referred to as the *changer*) and for anyone seeking to assist a peer with wellness goals (referred to as the *mentor or*

Wellness Mentor). Anyone can be both a changer and a mentor. This is the case with mutual support when two people help one another achieve a goal. Such mutual support is desirable in that it provides for a balanced relationship.

A similarity between conventional peer support and Wellness Mentoring is the source of assistance. Both forms of support are non-professional, and no particular health knowledge or expertise is assumed. Additional similarities include the spirit of generosity and goodwill that is embodied in helping a peer. Although you may be among the fortunate few who have high-quality peer support, it is likely that you and your friends, family and coworkers are not getting the support you need to achieve your goals. You can assess your own experience by taking one of the following *Peer Power Wellness Tests*. The first test is for those seeking to make a lifestyle change and the second test is for those focusing on how to assist.

The Changer's Peer Power Wellness Test

Assessing Your Support

This test is for someone already engaged in personal change. Think about your behavior change effort and the support you have received. Rate your level of agreement with the following peer support statements on the 5-point scale: (5) strongly agree, (4) agree, (3) undecided/don't know, (2) disagree, and (1) strongly disagree.

A friend, family member or coworker helped me:

5 4 3 2 1	Clarify and refine my behavior change goal.
5 4 3 2 1	Find a role model who had achieved my behavior change goal.
5 4 3 2 1	Identify and reduce barriers to the changes I was pursuing.
5 4 3 2 1	Find or create physical and social environments that supported my behavior change goal.
5 4 3 2 1	Get back on track when I faltered in pursuing my goal.
5 4 3 2 1	Celebrate the small and large steps made toward achieving my goal.
5 4 3 2 1	Experience ongoing, regular, and confidential support in my change efforts.

Scoring

Add up your score. There are 35 possible points. What is your Peer Power Wellness Support Level? If you are like most people, the support was modest, inconsistent or inadequate (or all three). A good score would be 28 or higher. It is highly unlikely that your support network delivered a complete array of emotional and instrumental assistance. *Not Alone* was written to close these gaps by teaching how to give and to get effective support. Your peers could have used Wellness Mentoring to shore up the support available for your wellness efforts.

The Mentor's Peer Power Wellness Test

Assessing Your Supportiveness

This test is for someone who has assisted with behavior change. Think about your peer support efforts. Rate your level of agreement with the following peer support statements on the 5-point scale: (5) strongly agree, (4) agree, (3) undecided/don't know, (2) disagree, and (1) strongly disagree.

I helped my peer:

5 4 3 2 1	Clarify and refine his behavior change goals.
5 4 3 2 1	Find a role model who had achieved the behavior change goal.
5 4 3 2 1	Identify and reduce barriers to the changes.
5 4 3 2 1	Find or create physical and social environments that supported the behavior change goal.
5 4 3 2 1	Get back on track when he faltered in pursuing his goal.
5 4 3 2 1	Celebrate the small and large steps made toward achieving the goal.
5 4 3 2 1	By offering ongoing, regular, and confidential support for his change efforts.

Scoring

Add up your score. There are 35 possible points. What is your Peer Power Wellness Supportiveness Level? Few people offer a complete array of support to a peer. If you are like most people, the support you offered was modest, inconsistent or inadequate (or all three). A good score would be 28 or higher. Don't be discouraged, however, as few people offer a complete array of support to a peer. *Not Alone* was written to close these gaps by teaching how to give effective support. Familiarity with Wellness Mentoring will assure that your peers enjoy the full benefits of your effective support.

As you can see by reading the questions in the *Peer Power Wellness Tests*, the focus of Wellness Mentoring is on expanding and strengthening support options. The approach is grounded in good science and has been field-tested in a variety of business and community wellness programs.

The primary lessons embedded in *Not Alone* were first developed for Union Pacific Railroad. Employees were trained to be Wellness Mentors so they could assist coworkers throughout the company's 36,000-plus mile track network. The Wellness Mentor Program™ is now used in hospitals and universities, as well as in government, church and businesses settings in North America, Africa, Latin America, Europe and Australia. Many of the lessons learned in these wellness programs have been incorporated into this book. You can purchase these programs via tutorials at www.wellnessmentor.net.

A systematic approach makes Wellness Mentoring more effective than the support available to most people. Wellness Mentoring expands your peer support tool options and explores a broad array of peer support objectives that have been validated by research. Practice tips feature quick and effective actions that address specific peer support challenges. Case stories illustrate key ideas. Checklists help you determine that you have covered all the important bases. Worksheets at the end of each chapter make it easier to quickly review key ideas with your peer.

Each chapter of *Not Alone* addresses additional peer support strategies. Although it is not necessary that you progress from chapter to chapter in the order they are presented, it is useful to use the subject matter and assignments found in each chapter as the focus for weekly mentoring sessions. The first chapter sets the stage for effective support, including how to explain the Wellness Mentoring concept, establish trust, set ground rules, and how to plan future sessions. The focus then turns to six primary support objectives.

The objectives are topics for weekly support sessions. Each support objective is examined in a *Not Alone* chapter:

1. **Setting Goals.** The focus is on clarifying wellness goals, exploring related scientific knowledge and tailoring personal goals. Both short- and long-term goals are set so they are compatible with the likely behavior change process.

2. **Identifying Role Models.** The focus is on finding someone who has achieved similar wellness goals under similar circumstances. Such a role model would be interviewed to learn more about what worked, what challenges were overcome and other tips that might be useful.

3. **Eliminating Barriers to Change.** Potential physical and psychological barriers are identified. Strategies are developed for breaking down barriers and for overcoming them. The approach to barriers is positive with an emphasis on existing strengths and finding the resources needed for success.

4. **Locating Supportive Environments.** Physical and social environments (at work, at home and in the community) are examined to determine how they support or undermine success. Strategies are developed for limiting contact with less supportive environments and increasing contact with environments that better support wellness goals.

5. Working through Relapse. No one wants to get off
track and fail to achieve desired behavior change. Game
plans are developed for avoiding high-risk situations and
for handling a relapse. As a result, the changer will be in
a position to learn from these experiences and to make
appropriate adjustments.

6. Celebrating Success. Most successes go unrecognized.
This is unfortunate because it is a missed opportunity
for some fun and because rewards reinforce behavior
change. The changer and mentor will identify many
occasions to celebrate as well as determine the most
meaningful way to make successes count.

I've tried to keep *Not Alone* focused and practical so you can
spend less time reading and more time achieving or supporting
wellness goals. I've also made the format suitable for nearly any
conceivable wellness goal that involves behavior change. You may
be surprised that I have not devoted more pages to the merits of
wellness goals. If you desire more information on that, John Travis,
author of the *Wellness Workbook* and an editor of *Not Alone,* offers
descriptions of the many ways we can integrate wellness into our
lives in his book.

A great deal of useful information is also widely available about
the health and economic benefits of physical activity, maintaining a
healthy weight, stopping smoking, and other lifestyle changes, so I
won't cover that information. I'm assuming you are already motivated.
The primary contribution of the book is to make peer support for
achieving wellness goals less threatening, more useful, more available
and, of course, more enjoyable.

Wellness Mentoring Stories

- Isaac uses Wellness Mentoring to address his tendency to overwork. At age 41 he already has high blood pressure and panic attacks. A long commute and pressure at work make it difficult for him to enjoy a balanced life.

- As the Director of Corporate Wellness at a supermarket chain with 7,500 employees, Josh sees Wellness Mentoring as a way to lift his company's employees out of a cycle of behavior change failure. The company has been offering wellness programs to its employees for a number of years, but participation has dropped off and the cost-effectiveness of the program is below expectations. Josh will make *Not Alone* a holiday gift to each employee and provide follow-up with online Wellness Mentor Training in order to reinforce the ideas in the book (see www.wellnessmentor.net).

- Yolanda and her friend Alice are using *Not Alone* to guide them in their efforts of mutual support. Both friends have been on nearly every diet, but can't seem to keep the weight off. They are using Wellness Mentoring techniques because they can't bear to suffer another failed attempt. They both want to be truly helpful and successful.

- Dr. Melina now uses Wellness Mentoring in her family medicine practice. She had stopped offering behavior change advice to her patients because she noticed that most were not making the changes she recommended, and it was easier to just prescribe medications and recommend surgery. Making *Not Alone* available to her patients has brought wellness back into her medical practice as she now feels more comfortable offering behavior change advice her patients can really use.

Step 1

Building the Foundation for Wellness Mentoring

Take a few minutes to reflect upon what it might really take to set the stage to support a peer in a successful health behavior change. Could it happen in a conversation in the next few minutes, or would it take a dozen or more follow-up conversations? Will the changer feel safe enough to share what he's planning to do if confidentiality is not first discussed? Can a helper be truly helpful without first taking some time to research the relevant facts and to organize input and follow-up questions? Obviously, a helper could push ahead and offer some "off the top of my head" reactions and that might be the end of it. But the helper could, instead, determine that she would like to make a profound contribution to this person's life. The helper could decide that she really wants this person to succeed and that she will do all she can to support a successful lifestyle change.

To step up to this higher level of peer support, both changer and helper need to lay a foundation for their relationship that establishes roles and responsibilities that go beyond more casual and everyday helping. The helper will need to move from a more casual and less organized support role to a mentor role that offers more organized support and follow-through.

Several building blocks offer a good foundation for stepping up to this higher level of mentoring support: (1) clarifying the mentor role, (2) selecting a peer for the mentor role, (3) building trust, (4) making an emotional connection, (5) establishing the logistics for an ongoing conversation about lifestyle change, and (6) creating a mechanism for checking whether mentoring is becoming unhelpful. These are the subjects of this chapter and make good subjects for the first week of wellness mentoring conversations.

Clarifying the Wellness Mentoring Role

Four qualities tend to set the Wellness Mentoring role apart from other forms of informal and non-paid support.

- ☝ **Creating a safe and caring relationship for exploring wellness goals.** This requires establishing trust and working to keep communications open, positive and guilt-free.

- ☝ **Asking questions that are useful in planning lifestyle change.** The mentor does more listening than telling. The mentor will be asking for clarification and reflecting back what she has heard. Those engaged in Wellness Mentoring are more likely to offer more thought-provoking questions than advice.

- ☝ **Seeking out resources for achieving lifestyle goals.** The mentor will utilize her contacts and ingenuity to get useful information and to break down barriers. You may, for example, join your peer in going to the library, surfing the Internet or attending a seminar. You may also join in brainstorming solutions to barriers to change such as a lack of time or money.

- ☝ **Embracing the learning and growth that come from someone's wellness journey.** The mentor's primary concern is avoiding negative judgments and, instead, supporting her peer in taking actions that are heartfelt and truly reflect personal choice.

The Wellness Mentor role has its origins in Homer's ancient Greek epic poem *The Odyssey*. Odysseus, the king of Ithaca, had a problem. He was leaving to fight in the Trojan War and needed to find someone who could help his independent-minded son, Telemachus, learn to be a king. Odysseus chose a man named Mentor because he saw that Mentor had special skills. Recognizing that his personal experiences would have limited value, Mentor taught by asking questions. Mentor also saw the value of learning through personal exploration. In this way, Mentor encouraged Telemachus to pursue his natural inclinations. Telemachus was also encouraged to change directions based on what he was learning. Mentor's strategy worked. Telemachus went on to become a helpful son and leader.

As in Homer's *The Odyssey*, offering effective Wellness Mentoring does not require direct personal experience with a particular wellness goal. Instead it occurs through the mutual embrace of the learning and growth of a personal wellness journey. Assistance comes primarily in the form of thought-provoking questions rather than advice. You recognize that knowledge unfolds during the process of change. The mentor has faith that her peer can and, most often, will find the best path to his own wellness.

The Wellness Mentor role is different from other support roles. While a counselor or therapist is focused on the deeper psychological causes underlying a behavior, Wellness Mentoring focuses on the practical aspects of health behavior change. The mentor may help her peer to find a counselor if deeper and more mysterious problems are identified that need attention.

Although teachers and personal coaches are professionals who guide people with their expertise in a particular area, the mentor does not claim to be a counseling or health expert. The mentor will ask questions designed to guide her peer toward determining his own best directions, rather than saying what she thinks is the best direction. You will join together in seeking out useful information from reliable sources.

Unlike professional helping roles, the mentor will not be compensated financially for Wellness Mentoring. While family members, housemates, coworkers and friends tend to offer impromptu/spontaneous/occasional encouragement, you will meet regularly with your peer to discuss progress toward health behavior change. Most of the focus will be on assisting with follow-through.

Choosing a Wellness Mentor

Selecting someone to be a primary support person is a critical step in Wellness Mentoring. You will be working together over an extended period of time – at least a couple of months. The following five questions are a good place to start when selecting a mentor.

- **Is the person a peer?** Peer are equals – a friend, a coworker, a housemate, a family member, a neighbor, a member of a group or organization to which you belong.

- **Do you think you can establish a high level of trust with this person?** This person should not be trying to sell you something nor be someone you cannot confide in.

- **Is this person enthusiastic about the wellness goal?** You don't need to agree on all the details about what will be achieved and how to get there, but you need to know that there is agreement that this effort is worthwhile. You will benefit from that positive energy going forward.

- **Will it be possible to meet with this peer on a weekly basis?** Ideally, you should be able to meet face-to-face for an hour. Does this person have time to commit and is she able to get to a face-to-face meeting?

- **Does this person seem like a good listener?** You do not want someone who can't hear you through or will do most or all the talking.

Note that the mentor need not be working on a wellness goal. And the mentor need not have achieved a similar wellness goal before. It would be great if you were to take turns offering support, but this mutual support situation is not assumed.

Once candidates have been selected, it's time to ask for assistance. The changer should explain about her wellness goal and explain that she is looking for a peer to offer follow-up support during a weekly face-to-face conversation. Give the mentor candidate at least one day to consider his decision. A loaner copy of *Not Alone* could be provided to the candidate. Reading the first two chapters will give the candidate a sense of the mentor role.

Establishing Trust

Supporting successful health behavior goals usually requires a high level of trust. For many of us this prerequisite can be unsettling. Weren't we taught as children not to trust others? Weren't we taught that change was somehow more valuable if we could claim that we had "done it all by ourselves." Didn't we learn somewhere that needing others is a sign of personal weakness?

As it turns out, many of these fundamental childhood lessons about distrusting others and not needing them undermine successful behavior change. For this reason, one of the first Wellness Mentoring skills is learning how to establish and maintain trust.

In order to make the concept of trust more manageable, it is helpful to break it down into types of trust. The four Cs of trust are these:

1. Contextual Trust

2. Communication Trust

3. Contractual Trust

4. Competence Trust

Contextual Trust

Contextual trust means that our relationship with our peer has a broad basis of familiarity. As we get to know the history and special interests of others, we can begin to appreciate and trust them more. Sometimes this form of trust is established through years of shared life experiences. This could be true of long-time friends or family members. However, all too often, people spend years working and living side-by-side without really knowing very much about the others' range of experiences. At work, for example, we may know a peer's specific task or job responsibility without knowing anything about family life, hobbies and personal aspirations.

When thinking about contextual trust, think about the relationship-building skills of successful salespeople. A successful salesperson, sitting down with a customer, does not immediately make sales pitches unless the customer insists. Instead, she opens with a discussion of common personal interests such as hobbies, family responsibilities or sports. She knows that in order to negotiate the best business deal, they must build trust. In a similar way, we should not leap into giving or getting support for health behavior change. First establish a relationship.

Activity for Establishing Contextual Trust

One way to quickly establish contextual trust is by taking turns answering "getting to know you" questions. You may want to use the "getting to know you" questions here to help establish trust. Try to share meaningful personal experiences and perspectives without venturing into what should really remain private. Sharing such experiences should be optional – only answer those questions you feel comfortable with.

Tell each other about
- Places you have lived

- A major change you have made

- Something that would help anyone understand you better

- A childhood experience that has had a lasting effect on you

- A person who has had an important impact on you

- How you chose your present work

- An experience in the last year or two that made a significant impression on you

- An obstacle you've overcome

- A significant personal achievement

- Your hobbies and special interests

By broadening the basis of a relationship, we will feel more comfortable expressing our true feelings and be better able to give and receive constructive feedback. With mutual and broader knowledge of one another, the person receiving the feedback is more likely to experience feedback as given in the spirit of being helpful. In contrast, if all we know about a person is related to one unhealthy behavior, then feedback about that behavior often feels like a criticism of the whole person. When constructive suggestions or probing questions are offered in the context of a broad relationship, then it's less likely to feel like a criticism.

Communication Trust

Communication trust refers to the willingness to disclose relevant information. It also refers to using your peer's personal information in a considerate way. When it comes to giving and receiving support for lasting behavior change, accurate and complete information is essential. If you withhold your true feelings, the quality and quantity of support is undermined. In contrast, when communication trust is high, information flows freely. There are five key concepts that build – or detract from – your communication trust:

Confidentiality Agreements

Agreements about privacy help to build trust by outlining how and when personal information may be shared with others. When supporting a health behavior goal, there will be times when it could be useful to get input from outside sources. In order to maintain communication trust, you share information only in a way that has been previously agreed to.

Establish your confidentiality guidelines early. Establish broad guidelines and then check in if unanticipated situations arise. The following guidelines will help you get started. You may want to add a couple of special situations where personal beliefs, rules or laws dictate the disclosure of information. For example, if you as mentor were working with a school bus driver, you may want to state up front that if the conversation indicates that drinking or other drugs are being used at work, you would find it necessary to contact the employee assistance program or other authorities about the need for assistance. The key is to discuss this limitation to confidentiality in advance. The following guidelines are a good starting place. You may need to add conditions (as the example of helping a school bus driver shows).

Suggested Confidentiality Guidelines

- ✎ I recognize that my ability to provide support depends on your confidence and trust in me.

- ✎ I recognize that what you tell me is in confidence.

- ✎ I will not disclose anything you tell me to anyone without first getting your permission unless you say that you will be committing suicide or physically harming yourself or someone else.

- ✎ I will never use the information you give me against you in any way.

The Concept of Need to Know

As we saw in the discussion of contextual trust, it is helpful to get to know each other. However, there are aspects of people's lives that should remain private. Where possible, confine your questioning and probing to relevant information. Encourage your peer to keep conversations focused on wellness goals. Keeping communication purposeful and on subject will help maintain communication trust.

The Obligation to Disclose

Withholding pertinent information or giving false information undermines communication trust. When it comes to behavior change, slips and setbacks can feel embarrassing. Most hunches and feelings are better disclosed and are usually worth exploring even if they are unfounded. Even when information is unflattering, the changer is responsible for telling his whole truth. Likewise, the mentor must explain herself fully. Working through hunches and feelings is a good way to establish and maintain trust.

Acknowledging Misunderstandings and Mistakes

A certain amount of trial and error comes with innovation. It is highly likely that you will misinterpret, not communicate well or be misunderstood. It is best to acknowledge such errors, apologize, explain what you have learned, and work toward new understanding. In most situations, there is little value in dwelling on mistakes, but it is important to acknowledge such errors before moving on. This builds trust and enables you to move forward with a minimum of residual baggage.

Attentive Listening

The way we listen enhances or undermines communication trust. We need to know that we are being heard and that our input is being given thoughtful consideration. This can be accomplished by looking at the person speaking, asking for clarification and checking to see if you fully understand what is being said. Bring your focus to what is being said. Try to avoid jumping to conclusions or judging before your peer has an opportunity to fully explain and you have had a chance to digest the information. It's okay to offer your initial reactions, but acknowledge that these are in fact first impressions and not any well-thought-out conclusions. Open your mind to your peer's way of seeing things. Offer your perspective in the spirit of kindness, mutual acceptance and the desire to be truly helpful.

Contractual Trust

Contractual trust is developed when peers come to agreement about how their relationship will function. This doesn't mean that rules are set in stone, but it does mean that the helping relationship will be organized in such a way that it respects time and other commitments. For example, it is important to establish how often to meet. You may also need to consider how long you will continue to meet before you will adjust or end your support sessions. Maintaining a schedule, sticking with it and showing up on time are all examples of how to build contractual trust.

Contractual trust includes full disclosure of any benefits or compensation. The mentor should explain why she is offering assistance. The reason can be as straightforward as the desire to care for others. If she is assisting because she has received similar help in the past, telling that story is likely to build contractual trust. If she is seeking to develop skills for a future helping profession career, that should be disclosed. Any form of anticipated compensation should be disclosed.

Competence Trust

Competence trust involves respecting people's knowledge, skills, abilities and judgments. To establish this form of trust, you must be clear about your strengths and limitations. For example, as a mentor, you should let your peer know if you have little formal training or experience with an issue that has been raised. An offer of support should not be mistaken for an unspoken declaration that the mentor knows very much about a peer's goals and how they are best achieved. Frank disclosure of experience (or the lack thereof) enhances competence trust.

In a similar way, the changer can help establish competence trust by revealing any knowledge, skills and abilities, or the lack thereof. Even without experience and knowledge about a given goal, the changer will build competence trust by enthusiastically pursuing and applying new knowledge and skills useful in long-term behavior change.

It is not enough to declare a lack of familiarity, knowledge or skills. The mentor can build trust by accompanying your peer to a library, bookstore or other information source to get needed information. She will build competence trust by actively pursuing useful information. Reading this book together is an example of how to build competence trust.

Trust Building Summary and Action Steps

1. Get your relationship off to a good start by taking time to get to know your peer and letting your peer get to know you. Later, take a couple of minutes during each meeting to learn something new about each other. This builds contextual trust.

2. Develop clear standards for confidentiality. Explain upfront whenever it appears necessary to go beyond your relationship for outside assistance.

3. Stay on task with your questions. Successful behavior change requires focus. By keeping to "need to know" information you will build communication trust as well as contractual trust.

4. Acknowledge mistakes and clear up misunderstandings.

5. Get clear about why you are doing this. The joy of helping can be its own reward. However, it is fine to help for a variety of reasons, as long as you are upfront about this.

6. Know and share your limits. How much time can you reasonably devote to this? Three months is a typical timeframe for a first round of peer support. Pick a date when you will check-in to determine if additional support meetings are warranted.

7. Make commitments you can keep. Showing up on time, responding promptly to calls and emails, re-scheduling only for absolute emergencies and following through on "homework" between meetings will make you a dependable partner.

8. What do you bring to the table? Sharing what you bring will help to establish competence trust. Maybe you have some specific experiences, knowledge or expertise that are relevant. Maybe you are offering your enthusiasm and a willingness to learn.

9. Determine the knowledge and experience level of your peer with respect to the change desired. Sometimes people have extensive experience in what's required, based on previous efforts.

Making the Emotional Connection

A spirit of love, kindness and generosity provides a good foundation for support. This spirit comes from the heart and is rooted in your own developmental experience and outlook. Although the spirit of support may seem a little abstract, you can sense your attitude toward giving and getting support. The following questions will help you examine your psychological orientation toward support.

Emotional Connection Indicator

Instructions: This indicator is designed for someone who has a history with peer support. You may, for example, answer the questions as they apply to a current Wellness Mentoring relationship. If, however, you are new to peer support, you may have to use your intuition about how you might experience such support. Think about your attitudes and experience of peer support. Rate your level of agreement with the following peer support statements on the 5-point scale: (5) strongly agree, (4) agree, (3) undecided/don't know, (2) disagree, and (1) strongly disagree.

In my peer support relationships:

5 4 3 2 1	Support is requested and given with ease and enthusiasm. The changer feels able to explain her situation and ask for help. The mentor, in turn, looks forward to being of assistance and gladly agrees to be of service.
5 4 3 2 1	You enjoy each other's company. You share both lighter and more serious moments.
5 4 3 2 1	You both feel comfortable saying what is on your mind. Open communication is a big asset in effective support.
5 4 3 2 1	You really *listen* to each other. You focus on what is being said, refrain from interrupting, ask for clarification and reflect back what you have heard to be sure that you heard correctly.
5 4 3 2 1	You maintain adult-to-adult communication. This means that setbacks and guilt do not generate communications that are more typical of a parent disciplining a child than a peer supporting a peer.
5 4 3 2 1	The mentor embraces the peer's wellness goal. Sometimes a changer chooses a goal that at first glance seems inappropriate or even foolish. The mentor shows faith and respect for the changer's desires and recognizes that goals often evolve in positive ways.
5 4 3 2 1	The mentor is caring and not overbearing. The mentor recognizes that the changer needs to develop her own goals and strategy. The mentor sees that sometimes he needs to step back to allow this to happen by substituting kindness, understanding and compassion for pressure, expressions of impatience or disappointment.

Scoring the Emotional Connection Indicator

Add up your score. There are 35 possible points. How was your emotional connection? Don't be discouraged if you don't initially get a 5 on each statement, or if some of these do not come naturally to you. Most of us have personal styles or attitudes that could undermine our abilities to achieve the ideal. Address any deficits by making a special effort or by developing strategies to limit their impact.

Acknowledging your strengths and weaknesses upfront may help you and your peer to adjust. You may want to suggest that your peer let you know when one of your "identified weaknesses" is getting in the way of your relationship. Hopefully, you and your peer will be quick to forgive when necessary. There are limits, however.

If you have problems with most, or all, of these characteristics of effective support, consider that you may not be the right person to offer Wellness Mentoring – at least with this person. A changer who has difficulty making one-on-one emotional connections may want to seek out a support group. Another creative, but less powerful, strategy for a changer who cannot connect emotionally is to become your own imaginary support person. Read this book and ask yourself what your imaginary mentor might say or do.

Setting Wellness Mentoring Logistics

When, where and how to meet are important logistical considerations. You will want to come up with a plan that best fits the needs for both mentor and changer.

Establishing the Format

Ideally, you and your peer will have face-to-face conversations. Such face time provides more complete communication. Facial gestures and body language communicate a lot. Your presence also says a lot about your high level of personal investment and engagement. Attention span is also increased in face-to-face communication. We are less likely to multi-task and more likely to listen carefully to someone in our presence. Another benefit of getting together with your peer is physical contact. A handshake and a hug bring us closer together physically and emotionally. They reinforce statements of agreement and our goodwill.

For all these reasons, you two should commit to at least some face-to-face conversations. Pick places that are convenient, maintain confidentiality, are relatively free of distracting noise and interruptions and consistent with your wellness goals. Private offices, a booth in an empty restaurant, a picnic table and a walking trail have all served this purpose. To avoid confusion and for increased comfort, try to stick with no more than a couple of places.

Technology brings a multitude of additional communication formats. Email, telephones and Internet chat offer ways to supplement in-person conversations. These are particularly handy when travel is difficult and time is tight. These high-tech and low-touch methods are also helpful in emergencies. There may be times when your peer needs immediate support to get through a particularly challenging day or experience. Email and postal mail is nice in that for some people the process of writing helps thinking and commitment processes. Sometimes the emotional distance of writing or a telephone call allows for greater disclosure.

You two should discuss possible communication strategies. Remember that you both must feel comfortable with the format. This may not be the time to learn or teach new communication technologies.

Setting Frequency

Wellness Mentoring is achieved through an ongoing conversation about health behavior change. Momentum is important. Meet weekly with breaks for holidays, illnesses and family emergencies.

Give your meetings the same priority normally given to work commitments. Other forms of communication such as phone calls and email can supplement your weekly meetings on an as-needed basis.

Wellness Mentoring conversations should last between 45 minutes and an hour. This will increase the likelihood that your focus will stay on behavior change and support. Although there are no hard and fast rules for how to organize this time, aim to divide up the conversation into relationship building, old business and new business.

Each of you should spend time each week sharing a little about your life. This will help balance the conversation. You may even add a ritual to the conversation such as a quick sharing of highs and lows for the week. Another example would be to exchange a favorite joke. Time should be spent on catching-up on progress and a review of the past weeks' discussions. Time should also be devoted to discussing a new way to build support. So, for example, a conversation would begin with a review of the prior week's discussion of health behavior goals and then turn to a discussion of how to identify and work with role models.

One advantage of conversations between peers is that they can continue as long as they are helpful. It is useful, however, to have check-in points so that Wellness Mentoring conversations do not feel like an endless commitment. Two months is a good initial commitment. This will give you an opportunity to discuss most, if not all, the six different support objectives of helping to set goals, identifying role models, eliminating barriers, locating supportive environments, working through relapse and celebrating success. This timeframe will also afford adequate time to make progress on behavior change goals. You two should pick a date to discuss progress and the value of continuing to meet. At that time you may also determine that additional conversations can be achieved through other formats such as phone calls and email.

Determining If Helping Is Still Helpful

From time to time it will be important to assess your Wellness Mentoring relationship. Most help is given with the best of intentions. At its best, assistance from a peer is offered with an open heart, with no hidden agendas and no expectation for compensation. But, at some point, helping may become a strain for either or both the mentor and the changer. The following questions can identify whether you have passed the point where assistance is helpful.

- **Are you feeling overcommitted?** Getting or giving help should not feel like a burden. You should be able to maintain your own wellness and personal priorities. Do not let over-commitment lead to a lack of follow-through. If you are overcommitted, you are probably giving less than your full attention to the desired change. If resentment is replacing kindness or receptivity, it's time to reassess.

- **Does it seem as if the mentor is superior or more powerful?** In American culture there has been a tendency to look down on people who need help. It is difficult, given this tradition, to view those being helped as equals. It is difficult to refrain from using help as a rationale for having power over a peer. This "power over" relationship is very unhealthy for both of you. It is better to pull back if inequality is felt by either.

- **Does it seem as if dependency is developing in the relationship?** There is a line beyond which helping undermines capabilities. The changer needs to come up with solutions to his problems. The changer cannot be spoon fed solutions. The changer needs to do most of the research and other work, if he is to gain a sense of responsibility. He needs to own his decisions and feel free to change his mind without the mentor's permission. If either feels as if a line has been crossed that is now crimping the changer's style and undermining independence, it is time to reassess.

- **Is the mentor doing more telling than listening?**
  Effective peer support primarily involves asking useful questions and listening, not being a "know it all." Look at the balance of questions and advice. If the mentor is not asking many more questions, the relationship may have tipped into disempowerment mode. If the changer has grown tired of advice, there is not enough listening happening. Change the mix.

- **Have either become obsessed about success?**
  Wellness goals are important, but it is okay to move on to other issues or delay a change for a little while. If either is becoming angry, frustrated or annoyed about lack of progress, it's time to reassess.

- **Have dishonesty and a lack of trust crept into the relationship?** Sometimes guilt, shame and embarrassment undermine helping. Maybe one or both mentor and changer have not followed through on their commitments. Maybe one or both have decided that it is better to look good than to tell the truth. No matter what the reason, if you cannot rebuild trust, it's time to reassess.

If your answers to these questions lead you to feel that helping is no longer helpful, it is time to talk about this with your peer. Maybe she will be relieved that this issue has been brought out into the open. Maybe your conversation will get your relationship on track. If your relationship has gotten too dysfunctional or complicated, propose that an alternative source of help be found such as another person willing to help. The changer may also like to proceed without assistance. Don't stick it out if it does not feel good to either one of you. More of the same will not help.

Wellness Mentoring Stories

- John and Jack have great respect for each other as well as a budding friendship. They were introduced through a workplace Wellness Mentoring initiative. Employees were invited to attend an orientation session, paired-up and provided a copy of *Not Alone* to help guide their mutual support efforts. Both men wanted to quit smoking. They spent most of their first meeting sharing their personal stories. They quickly agreed to keep their conversations confidential except in cases where someone might be injured. Although it took some hunting, they found a quiet nearby smokefree café to conduct their Tuesday lunchtime meetings. They also agreed to keep meeting through New Year's Day, as this would be a challenging time for their smoking cessation efforts.

- Alice asked her best friend, Jody, to use Wellness Mentoring to help her restore balance after a recent divorce. She gave Jody a copy of *Not Alone* to guide the process. They agreed to keep their conversation in confidence and to take a walk on Wednesday evenings to discuss Alice's goals. Fortunately, they already had a trusting relationship to build upon.

- Jim and Joyce had been married for six years when they decided to make some personal changes using Wellness

Mentoring. Jim wants to lose some pounds and Joyce wants a regular fitness routine. They agreed to hold a special Wellness Mentoring conversation on Thursday nights after their kids were in bed. They also agreed not to discuss their efforts with other family and friends without first getting permission from each other.

- Sabrina finds conversations difficult and prefers the anonymity of a group. She took the Emotional Connection Indicator and quickly realized that working with someone in such an intense way was not for her. Rather than seeking a peer for support, she decided to join a support group at work and to use Wellness Mentoring with the group. After all, she reasoned, these people could help me set goals and many of the veteran members could serve as role models.

- Al and Brendan met at a health spa where they were introduced to Wellness Mentoring. Brendan was going through a difficult divorce and was struggling to "get his groove back." Al was exploring his spiritual side and wanted to practice daily meditation. Al felt strongly that Brendan should also meditate. He saw this as the best way to handle feelings about the divorce. Brendan, on the other hand, wanted to pursue a more active social life combined with more physical activity. After their third meeting, Brendan confronted Al about not being open to his wellness goals. Al pushed back and acknowledged that he felt the meditation would do the trick. Brendan told Al that he did not feel the helping relationship was working and asked that they call it quits.

Building the Foundation Checklist

Before turning to the next chapter on help with goal setting, make sure you have built a good Wellness Mentoring foundation. The following checklist will help you determine whether you have covered the core pillars.

☐ We are both clear about the roles and responsibilities of a Wellness Mentoring relationship. We see how this support differs from other forms of helping.

☐ We have a plan for how often and where we shall meet.

☐ We have identified a good ending date for this round of support.

☐ Our discussions feel helpful and comfortable.

☐ We have agreed-upon rules for confidentiality including when we may need to break confidentiality for outside assistance.

☐ We will keep track of our Wellness Mentoring relationship to assure that it is a good helping relationship.

Worksheet for Step 1

Wellness Mentoring Questions	Commentary
1. Picking a Wellness Mentor	
Is this person a peer?	Find an equal, someone who has a similar frame of reference and will continue to be available.
Can we establish a high level of trust?	Look at the potential for contextual, communication, competence and contractual trust. The Emotional Connection Indicator may also help assess this capacity.
Is this person enthusiastic about your overall wellness goals?	Enthusiasm generates energy and follow-through.
Does the person seem like a good listener?	Listening is the most important skill in Wellness Mentoring.
Will it be possible to meet on a weekly basis?	Regular meetings help maintain momentum.
2. Building Trust and Openness	
How will we really get to know each other?	This establishes contextual trust.
Do we have good communication?	Open and honest communication makes the relationship more powerful.
What are the limits of confidentiality?	Decide what rare situations would require breaking confidence (such as a situation in which physical harm or criminal activity is being contemplated).
Why is the mentor doing this?	Full disclosure of all the reasons for helping builds contractual trust.
What skill and experience, if any, do we have going into this?	Get clear about your skills, or lack thereof, to develop competence trust.
3. Making the Emotional Connection	
What strengths and limitations do we each have in forming emotional connections?	Take the Emotional Connection Indicator to bring these issues to light.

Worksheet for Step I (continued)

Wellness Mentoring Questions	Commentary
3. Making the Emotional Connection (continued)	
How will we manage emotional connection limitations?	Develop a strategy for coping with any limitations or agree that an option would be selecting a new support person if necessary.
4. Setting Wellness Mentoring Logistics	
When and where shall we meet?	Decide on a place that is relatively private, convenient and comfortable.
What format will we use to communicate?	Decide about in-person, telephone and email communication and any times when communication should be limited (such as not calling after 7:00 p.m.).
5. Determining if Helping Is Still Helpful	
Has the power in the relationship moved out of balance?	A Wellness Mentoring relationship requires thoughtful attention. The mentor and changer should feel equal. Feeling superior or more powerful is not appropriate for promoting wellness.
Has a dependency developed?	This is not a caretaker relationship. Helping should not undermine the capabilities of the changer.
Is the mentor listening well enough?	The mentor's primary responsibility is not to tell, but rather to listen and offer good questions.
Have we slipped into an obsession with success?	Keep wellness goals in perspective so they don't overwhelm other priorities and lead to irrational decisions.
Have we maintained trust?	Good communication and a good relationship depend on trust.

Step 2
Setting Goals

At first glance, most wellness goals seem fairly straightforward. In their most simple form, these goals are a description of desired wellness outcomes. For example, your peer might say, "I'm going to lose some weight," or "I'm going to deal better with the stress in my life."

When you ask for further clarification about the goal, it's easy if your peer knows the details of how, why and when the goal will be achieved. If your peer has identified some daily behaviors that will achieve the desired result, you can quickly agree upon benchmarks for success and develop a timeline for achieving those benchmarks.

If wellness goals are already well formed, then your assistance with goal setting will consist of a goals checkup. If, however, the goals are less focused and not fully formed, you will need to turn your attention to supporting the changer in clarifying, refining, integrating and prioritizing the goal(s).

This chapter explores some of the details that are embedded in goal setting. You will read how to set goals that are both meaningful and achievable and find strategies for creating these even when there is little clarity about the goal. You will read about how to set goals that are integrated with other priorities. You will learn about the stages of behavior change that move from initial resistance, through contemplation, preparation, action, maintenance and moving on to other challenges. You will also learn how to get the scientific facts about wellness goals and to separate these facts from wishful thinking, popular fads and marketing schemes. And finally, you will learn how to measure progress.

Embracing the Wellness Journey

Wellness is a process of continual growth. Goals evolve as competing priorities are in flux. Sometimes goals change because people gain new insights. Such changes could be the result of new scientific information or the result of personal experience. Sometimes goals change because the social influences have changed.

Embracing the wellness journey involves resistance to some changes and acceptance of others. Resist making changes that are born out of frustration with behavior change and lowered self-esteem. Embrace changes that reflect a more complete understanding and come from a position of strength and hopefulness. Making such determinations can be extremely difficult as many of our decisions fall into gray areas.

Integrating Priorities

Wellness goals often address a number of behaviors that overlap in such a way that one goal spills over into other goals. For example, someone wanting to lose weight may find this will be achieved by increasing physical activity, reducing job stress, sleeping better, and eating healthier foods.

To fully integrate wellness goals, they must be organized and prioritized. A better understanding of the breadth and scope of personal priorities will identify possible synergies and by take likely competing concerns into consideration.

The *Wellness Lifestyle Inventory* helps determine needs and priorities. It covers a broad range of possible goals within the areas of physical, social, economic and emotional wellness.

Wellness Lifestyle Inventory

Instructions: Most people can identify several wellness goals. This inventory helps identify some strengths and opportunities for improvement. For each question, you are interested in two issues. First, determine whether or not this wellness quality is already in place. Check the boxes for these strengths. Then, decide whether or not you would like to change this aspect of your life. In the second column, check the boxes associated with areas you would like to change.

EMOTIONAL WELLNESS	Achievement	Satisfaction
Rate your achievement and personal satisfaction with your current wellness.	**I already do this**	**I would like to change this**
Start your day rested and with a good attitude.	☐	☐
Rarely feel "blue."	☐	☐
Achieve a balance between work, rest and play.	☐	☐
Balance work and family/household responsibilities.	☐	☐
Rarely feel stress (less than a few times a week).	☐	☐
Take time during most days for prayer, meditation or reflection.	☐	☐
Feel your life is important.	☐	☐
Be in control of your own behavior.	☐	☐
Feel that you are basically a good person.	☐	☐
Feel good about how your body looks.	☐	☐
Use personal mistakes as opportunities to learn and grow.	☐	☐
Laugh regularly.	☐	☐
Find ways to make everyday or routine tasks interesting or satisfying.	☐	☐

EMOTIONAL WELLNESS CONTINUED	Achievement	Satisfaction
Rate your achievement and personal satisfaction with your current wellness.	**I already do this**	**I would like to change this**
Find times to kick back and relax.	☐	☐
Regularly do things that make you happy.	☐	☐
Celebrate personal accomplishments.	☐	☐
Approach life with honesty.	☐	☐
Explore your talents and interests.	☐	☐
Be open to new ideas and experiences.	☐	☐
Follow through on working toward your goals and dreams.	☐	☐
Be in touch with your inner feelings and motivations.	☐	☐
Develop your own sense of spirituality and meaning in your life.	☐	☐
Find ways to make a contribution to the world.	☐	☐
PHYSICAL WELLNESS	Achievement	Satisfaction
Rate your achievement and personal satisfaction with your current wellness.	**I already do this**	**I would like to change this**
Keep your body flexible through regular stretching.	☐	☐
Keep your muscles in tone through lifting weights or some sort of resistance workout.	☐	☐
Enjoy at least two forms of physical activity (such as biking, walking or swimming).	☐	☐
Keep your heart fit by taking part in 30 minutes or more of physical activity most days of the week.	☐	☐

PHYSICAL WELLNESS CONTINUED	Achievement	Satisfaction
Rate your achievement and personal satisfaction with your current wellness.	**I already do this**	**I would like to change this**
Not smoke.	☐	☐
Avoid smoky places.	☐	☐
Organize your home and/or work to avoid injury (including such things as lighting, lifting, and safety gear).	☐	☐
Wear a seat belt at all times when riding in a car.	☐	☐
Never ride in a car that is driven by someone (including yourself) who has been drinking or is driving recklessly.	☐	☐
For men: consume fewer than 12 drinks per week and fewer than 4 drinks on any single occasion, not exceeding 1 drink per hour.	☐	☐
For women: consume fewer than 9 drinks per week and fewer than 3 drinks on any single occasion, not exceeding 1 drink per hour.	☐	☐
Avoid activities that place you at high risk for AIDS (including unprotected sex with multiple partners and sharing needles).	☐	☐
Avoid non-prescription "recreational" drugs.	☐	☐
Eat foods that are low in fat.	☐	☐
Eat foods that are high in fiber.	☐	☐
Consume little, if any, caffeine.	☐	☐
Avoid eating refined sugar.	☐	☐
Find ways to prepare and enjoy meals consisting mainly of fruits, vegetables, nuts, whole grains and beans.	☐	☐
Be within 10 pounds of your ideal weight.	☐	☐

PHYSICAL WELLNESS CONTINUED	Achievement	Satisfaction
Rate your achievement and personal satisfaction with your current wellness.	**I already do this**	**I would like to change this**
Brush your teeth at least twice daily.	☐	☐
Floss your teeth daily.	☐	☐
Visit your dentist at least once a year for treatment or a check-up.	☐	☐
Undergo recommended health screenings and physicals.	☐	☐
Have at least one health professional with whom you feel comfortable discussing medical problems.	☐	☐
Look up needed medical recommendations at the library, in the bookstore or by computer.	☐	☐
Be a careful consumer of medical resources by getting second opinions where appropriate, following through on treatment plans and asking about costs.	☐	☐
ECONOMIC WELLNESS	Achievement	Satisfaction
Rate your achievement and personal satisfaction with your current wellness.	**I already do this**	**I would like to change this**
Sharpen your employment skills through continuing education, reading and discussing your work with others.	☐	☐
Ask for fair compensation for the work you do.	☐	☐
Speak up to stop mistreatment of yourself or coworkers.	☐	☐
Join with others in the workplace in eliminating unsafe products and consumer fraud.	☐	☐
Have a detailed personal financial plan that will achieve your short- and long-term goals.	☐	☐

ECONOMIC WELLNESS CONTINUED	Achievement	Satisfaction
Rate your achievement and personal satisfaction with your current wellness.	**I already do this**	**I would like to change this**
Organize your spending practices so that you live within your means.	☐	☐
Be in agreement about money matters with your spouse or domestic partner.	☐	☐
Comparison shop for the best combination of product, customer service and price.	☐	☐
Avoid materialism (that is, buying because of advertising, sales pressure or just to have what others have).	☐	☐
Save environmental resources and money by fixing and maintaining your possessions, recycling, and using less energy.	☐	☐
Pay your credit card bills in full.	☐	☐
Pay your rent or mortgage, utilities, taxes and car payments on time.	☐	☐
Save and invest at least 5 percent of your monthly income for retirement, education or a rainy day.	☐	☐
Have enough financial reserves (not including retirement savings) to last at least 6 months without employment.	☐	☐
Have enough investments or life insurance available in the event of your death to meet the living expenses and tuition of your children until they become adults.	☐	☐
Protect your investments through diversification and by funding your individual retirement account (IRA) or pension plan.	☐	☐

ECONOMIC WELLNESS CONTINUED	Achievement	Satisfaction
Rate your achievement and personal satisfaction with your current wellness.	I already do this	I would like to change this
Be sure you are getting a reasonable rate of return for the investment risks you are taking.	☐	☐
Have a close friend or family member who would come through for you if you had financial problems.	☐	☐
Be able to help friends and family members with financial problems.	☐	☐
Choose investments that reflect your personal values (such as environmental, social justice and non-violence).	☐	☐
Make purchases that reflect your personal values.	☐	☐
Make contributions to causes and charities that you believe in.	☐	☐
SOCIAL WELLNESS	Achievement	Satisfaction
Rate your achievement and personal satisfaction with your current wellness.	I already do this	I would like to change this
Develop, renew and maintain friendships.	☐	☐
Socialize with friends on a regular basis.	☐	☐
Have at least 2 close or intimate relationships.	☐	☐
Experience the love and affection you need.	☐	☐
Feel close to your family.	☐	☐
Introduce yourself and greet people you encounter.	☐	☐
Regularly get together with others to play games, enjoy friendly competitions, go to the movies or attend community/cultural events.	☐	☐

SOCIAL WELLNESS CONTINUED	Achievement	Satisfaction
Rate your achievement and personal satisfaction with your current wellness.	**I already do this**	**I would like to change this**
Value diversity (appreciating variety in backgrounds and beliefs).	☐	☐
See other people as basically good until proven otherwise.	☐	☐
Respond in times of others' needs.	☐	☐
Be a good listener.	☐	☐
Acknowledge your mistakes.	☐	☐
Resolve conflict in positive ways.	☐	☐
Cheer others on.	☐	☐
Share credit for success.	☐	☐
Celebrate the accomplishments of others.	☐	☐
Be honest.	☐	☐
Offer constructive feedback to others in a non-judgmental way.	☐	☐
Feel comfortable in social situations.	☐	☐
Feel comfortable taking a leadership role.	☐	☐
Team up well on tasks or projects.	☐	☐
Join a support group when faced with continuing (chronic) physical or emotional problems.	☐	☐

Interpreting Wellness Lifestyle Inventory Results

There is no good or bad score for the *Wellness Lifestyle Inventory*. Wellness is more about making conscious choices and working toward achieving full potential than it is about meeting a universal standard. The *Wellness Lifestyle Inventory* is designed to raise consciousness about the wide breadth of the wellness philosophy. The following recommendations are for possible follow-up discussions.

- **Review strengths.** Acknowledge wellness behavior that is already in place. Discuss these positive qualities with your peer. How can they be used to address any remaining opportunities for improvement? Explore how lifestyle strengths were developed. See if you can learn from past success experiences. Build upon these strengths when approaching issues that still need attention. Wellness strengths are important because they indicate past success and are the building blocks for future progress.

- **Review those areas that need attention.** It's okay if your answer indicates you do not practice a behavior and yet you are satisfied with the way things stand. It's probably better to look at the areas where there is a desire to change. The mentor should try not to impose an opinion, but ask questions to get clarification about the changer's understanding of these areas.

- **Examine any goals not covered in the Inventory.** Determine if all interests were adequately covered and discuss any gaps or variations that better reflect his personal interests.

- **Explore possible connections between goals.** Wellness is an integrative process that engages mind, body and spirit. By examining possible links among wellness goals, you may come up with new practices that address many goals simultaneously. For example, a daily yoga practice could address stress, flexibility and core body strength. A daily jog or walk could help address weight, cardiovascular health and emotional health. When done with friends, many health behaviors can also address social wellness goals. Go over the list of desired behavior changes with your peer and look for ways that any of these could simultaneously achieve a number of positive wellness goals. These changes could be given a higher priority.

- **Examine personal passion, motivation and enthusiasm for the goals.** Wellness goals need to be worthy of continued commitment. Sometimes these goals are called "Big Hairy Audacious Goals." Enthusiasm and drive make changes easier to maintain and more enjoyable. The best goals are not always the easiest.

- **Set priorities.** Most people have more than one wellness goal. Prioritize goals by discussing how much change should be taken on now, and whether or not some goals should be addressed later. Everyone has limits. Goals must be big enough to be challenging without feeling overwhelming.

Raise Awareness about the Benefits

Wellness goals tend to have benefits that go unrecognized. Once priority goals are identified, it can be useful to increase our awareness and appreciation for why they are so important.

The following four broad categories offer a way to categorize wellness benefits. Wellness goals are about:

- **Achieving healing, disease management, complementary/alternative/integrative medicine.** Sick people want to recover from or manage an illness, and restore vitality. A survivor of a heart attack may be pursuing new diets and fitness goals.

☙ **Preventing illness and reducing health risks.** A smoker realizes that he is likely to develop respiratory diseases, cancer and diabetes and has a greater susceptibility to colds so he decides to quit.

☙ **Improving quality-of-life.** A workaholic finds her job overwhelming and unfulfilling so she drops out of "the rat race" to pursue voluntary simplicity. She is now thriving again.

☙ **Attaining peak performance.** An athlete adopts a yoga routine to improve her ability to compete. An artist goes for a morning walk to enhance her creative energy.

With your peer, explore the purposes for achieving the wellness goal(s). Which of these wellness drivers are being engaged? Clarifying the primary motivations for change will also guide the type of information that will be useful in planning the change. A goal of regular exercise takes on very different characteristics if it is being used to address heart disease. The advice of a cardiac rehabilitation center is very different from the advice of a triathlon coach. It's best to get information that matches the wellness motivation even though the journey may later evolve to other wellness themes.

Understanding Social Context

Wellness goals are often heavily influenced by others. Social connections are important to wellbeing. They should be taken into consideration. What is the the social context of the wellness goal?

- **Pleasing others.** A son tries to lose weight because his mother is concerned about his health and his ability to attract a woman.

- **Fitting in or being more desirable.** A smoker attempts to quit so he can find a job in a smokefree company.

- **Caring and being responsible.** A father seeks to cut his risk of a heart attack so that he will live long enough to see his children grow up.

As can be seen in these examples, social motives can be complicated in that they are not under our direct control, and they may be mixed with shame, guilt, fear of rejection and the desire to rescue others. It is tempting to discount their importance and to recommend that people get over or move beyond such influences. But social forces, although complicated, are real and have consequences. They must be factored into any wellness goal.

Behavior change is a personal decision that should not be overridden by the preferences of others. To be responsible, we must take the needs of others into consideration, but we must also be responsible about living our lives in accordance with our own needs and passions. For example, a goal for stress management must fit with employment considerations. We can't just quit a stressful job without upsetting our economic wellness as well as the welfare of those who count on our paycheck. You and your peer should clarify how your wellness goals affect others.

Getting the Facts

Once you have full appreciation of the reasons to change, it is time to focus on available scientific information about the best approach. Try to separate facts from fiction by finding information that you have confidence in. The following key questions will help.

- Is the information supported by adequate research?

- Does the source have a reputation for accuracy or is it part of a sales pitch?

- Has the information held up over time and with repeated investigation?

- Is the information appropriate in terms matching up with age, sex and other characteristics of the changer?

You and your peer may need to go to a library, reputable Internet sites and health experts to get additional input about the appropriate behavioral goals and how they should be achieved.

Setting Measurable Goals

Do you have good ways to measure progress? Ideally, you will be able to regularly assess goal achievement. Measurement should have a behavioral component. For example, the goal might be to walk three miles most days of the week. Additional measures of progress should also be explored. For example, with a fitness goal, heart rate may also be a measure of success. Another example would be to be able to talk comfortably while maintaining a certain pace.

Working the Change Process

Lifestyle change is a process rather than an event. The process includes a number of sub-goals that add up to lasting behavior change. For example, a goal of staying on track has a different focus than does an initial goal of planning how best to begin the lifestyle change.

I've adapted Prochaska and DiClemente's six-stage model to create a useful behavior change map. Share this roadmap with your peer. Use it to determine the most likely current stage of change. If it is difficult to determine the stage of change, use the series of questions that follow this table to narrow down the alternatives.

The Process of Behavior Change

	Stage of Change	Appropriate Change Goal
1.	**Developing Commitment:** You are not truly convinced about the importance of the lifestyle goal. You may be just exploring the general possibility of taking on a particular goal. For example, someone might have told you such a goal is worthwhile.	You are unlikely to have formed a Wellness Mentoring relationship with someone at this stage. However, if you find yourself in the "exploratory phase," then the goal is to get more information about the value of such a change.
2.	**Contemplation:** You would like to change and think you will attempt change in the next six months.	You should set a date for making the change. If you find yourself in a peer relationship with someone at this early stage, engaging in conversation about the possibilities can often help solidify your thinking.
3.	**Preparation:** You are planning to take action in the immediate future (usually within the next month) and are determining the best strategy to carry out the change.	Develop the plan for how the change will be carried out. You should talk to others about your intention to change.
4.	**Action:** You are engaged in making changes.	Adjust to the new lifestyle and manage unexpected emotional and physical reactions.

The Process of Behavior Change (continued)

5.	**Maintenance:** You are working to integrate the behavior change into normal day-to-day life.	Continue to pay attention to the behavior and work through any relapse. The central focus is to get comfortable with the new behavior and have it become fully integrated into other aspects of life. At this point, it also helps for you to act as a mentor and to assist with similar goals.
6.	**Moving On:** You have maintained the change for a year or more, and you are never tempted by the old behavior.	Set new health-enhancing goals. Move on from support systems that are focused exclusively on the prior lifestyle goal. It no longer is useful to look at yourself as one step from relapse. You no longer want to define yourself around the old goal. It's time to move on to other wellness interests.

If it is not clear which stage of change you are in, the following questions can narrow down the possibilities.

Questions for Determining the Stage of Change

	Questions for the Changer	Likely Stage of Change
1.	Have you begun to adopt the new practice(s) that move(s) you toward your goal?	If yes, skip to question 4. If no, answer questions 2 and 3.
2.	Do you believe that changing this behavior is important to your personal health and well being?	If the answer is no, you are likely to be in the **Developing Commitment Stage.**
3.	When do you plan to start changing your behavior?	If you express a general interest in changing with no particular timetable, you are in the **Contemplation Stage.** If you have set a date to begin your behavior change, you are in the **Preparation Stage.**
4.	How long have you been practicing your new chosen behavior?	If you have begun the new behavior and have maintained the practice for less than six months, you are in the **Action Stage.** If you have practiced the new behavior for six months or more, you are either in the **Maintenance Stage** or in the **Moving On Stage.**
5.	Have you been tempted to practice the old unhealthy behavior in the past year?	If you are no longer tempted by the old behavior, you are likely to be in the **Moving On Stage.**

The six stages of change provide a useful roadmap for behavior goals. Use the stages to mark progress and then celebrate success. If things get off track, use the stages to see where the change effort has settled. The roadmap also keeps Wellness Mentoring conversations meaningful by narrowing the focus. For example, a conversation about how to get started that is appropriate in the preparation stage would not be as useful for a peer in the maintenance stage. In the maintenance stage, the focus would more likely be on issues such as how to manage a relapse or how to avoid high-risk situations.

Wellness Mentoring Stories

- Greg's mother has Alzheimer's. Greg has read numerous books on the subject and has received information from the Alzheimer's Prevention Foundation. He recently read a *New York Times* article that said exercise and taking aspirin regularly could prevent the disease. Greg now feels as if he is an Alzheimer's expert, but has yet to make a behavior change. Greg has talked about his goals with his officemate, Bill. They determined that Greg is ready to set a date to begin his exercise program. He is ready to add a 20-minute walk to his daily routine. They are satisfied that they have a plan that would address Greg's prevention goal.

- Jill wants to cut 10 minutes off her next marathon and qualify for the Boston Marathon. She asked for Wellness Mentoring support from her husband, Bob. They hunted for advice in a stack of recent *Runner's World* magazines and also reviewed a book by several top women marathoners. Jill and Bob used these sources to come up with a list of possible changes. They settled on incorporating some shorter speed workouts and upping the amount of daily stretching. They decided to wait until after the New Year's holiday to begin these changes.

- Stan is approaching retirement. He asked his friend Steve about his recent retirement and Steve suggested that they help one another make the transition. Stan and Steve completed the *Wellness Lifestyle Inventory*. Both men came up with some goals for each of its wellness dimensions. When setting priorities, Stan decided to focus on social wellness. He was particularly concerned that he would feel lonely without his work buddies. Steve identified economic wellness as his first priority. He hadn't anticipated that his post-work life would be so expensive, and he hoped he could find new activities that were less costly.

- Alice's heart attack was a wake-up call for her entire family. The hospital offered nutrition counseling, and Alice attended cardiac rehabilitation for the next month. Alice was getting good guidance from her medical team and was making progress to a full recovery. Alice's oldest daughter, Jen, was particularly concerned that Alice take all the right medications. Alice was happy to have Jen's Wellness Mentoring support, and they both attended a meeting with the nurse to go over each drug. Alice's husband, Jarid, wanted to help Alice lose weight and get an exercise routine going. After some Wellness Mentoring discussions, Jarid realized that Alice wasn't interested in exercise, but was excited about healthier eating. They looked over a number of weight-loss programs and settled on Weight Watchers because it had a good track record and seemed to match Alice's overall philosophy.

Goal-Setting Checklist

Before turning to the next chapter on identifying role models, summarize your goal-setting findings. The following checklist will help you determine whether you have covered the key ideas.

☐ We examined the overall wellness picture to reveal a range of wellness goals. We determined how some goals could be accomplished together.

☐ We prioritized the goals or determined which goal should happen first, second, third, and so on.

☐ We examined the underlying thrust of our wellness goals. We have determined if the goals are directed at (1) managing an illness, (2) lowering the risk of future health problems, (3) improving quality of life, or (4) achieving peak performance.

☐ We looked at the social context for the wellness goal and how relationships may be influencing decisions.

☐ We investigated the facts pertaining to the wellness goals. We identified the best sources of information available for setting specific, measurable, short-term and long-term goals. Our goals make the best use of available science and research. The approaches we are taking have shown their worth in situations similar to ours.

☐ We discussed the six stages of the behavior change process. We have benchmarks for moving along the stages toward our wellness goal(s).

Worksheet for Step 2

Wellness Mentoring Questions	Commentary
1. Embracing the Wellness Journey	
What are the behavior change goals of the changer?	Identify behavior change goals associated with emotional, physical, economic and social wellness.
What are the changer's strengths?	Identify strengths associated with emotional, physical, economic and social wellness.
Are there ways that current strengths can be applied to new wellness goals?	Strengths encourage forward movement.
Are there some actions that will address two or more behavior change priorities?	Many wellness activities such as yoga, stopping smoking and physical activity have a number of payoffs.
What wellness goals is the changer passionate about?	It takes energy and passion to achieve many goals.
Is the changer clear about what he would like to evenutally achieve.	Setting clear wellness priorities is essential to success.
2. Appreciating the Benefits	
What are the benefits of achieving the goal?	Keeping motivated is easier with a lot of good reasons. Determine all the health, healing, quality of life and social benefits of making the change.
3. Getting the Facts	
What do the experts say about this health behavior?	It is important to separtate fact from fiction and sales pitches.

Worksheet for Step 2 (continued)

Wellness Mentoring Questions	Commentary
4. Monitoring Progress	
How will progress be measured?	It is easier to see progress when goals are clear, specific and measurable. Such feedback keeps goals on track.
5. Working the Change Process	
What is the current stage of change?	Knowing the stage facilitates focusing on the tasks that are most meaningful.
What will indicate forward movement to another stage of change?	The stages form mini-goals and a roadmap for seeing progress as the behavior change unfolds.

Step 3
Identifying Role Models

Role models offer a window into a successful future. Why wait to see the benefits of change when others have already achieved the same or similar goals? Why not look at what has worked? Why not avoid some of the common mistakes and pitfalls? Why not get encouragement from someone who has walked in your shoes? Visualizing success through a role model can speed progress.

Mentors may find it a relief to know that they are not expected to be a changer's role model. It is unlikely and not necessary that the mentor has achieved the same or similar wellness goals. You can work with your peer to seek out one or more role models. You can help select the best role models. You can help take full advantage of a role model's experiences.

Exchanging Success Stories

Most of us have experiences that make us role models for behavior change. It is likely that your stories include successes that will inspire. Think about goals you have achieved and obstacles you have had to overcome. Your peer is also likely to have achieved some successes. Exchange stories, memories and recollections of times in your lives when you have achieved wellness goals.

- What was your wellness goal?

- What were the reasons you made the change?

- What strategies worked?

- What challenges did you overcome?

- How did other people help?

A Time for Bragging

To do this well, you have to abandon any inhibitions about bragging. Here's one of my stories of fitness glory. It's an example of a success story I might share in a Wellness Mentoring session:

I like to keep my exercise routine fresh by taking on new challenges. A few years ago, I set a wellness goal of participating in Ironman™ distance triathlons. These are very long races that begin with a 2.4-mile swim, then transition to a 112-mile bike ride and finish with a marathon run of 26.2 miles. This was a big stretch for me since a marathon run had been my longest achievement, and I was new to distance swimming and biking.

In order to develop my skills, I took a triathlon course at the University of Vermont and joined a master's swim club. I also read a helpful book by Steve Jonas, M.D., for aspiring triathletes. I was lucky to connect with several mentors including Jim Carman and Jim Baker. Both men had participated in several events. Jim Carman was a world-class champion, and Jim Baker was relatively new to Ironman events, having completed a couple in my geographic area. These men talked with me about my training plan and offered lots of encouragement. Jim Baker and I trained together. We focused on "bricks," which are training days that include two race elements (such as biking and running).

After five months of preparation, I competed in the Montreal event and finished fourth in my age group. Accepting my trophy at the awards ceremony was a great moment of joy that could never have been achieved without many supportive friends and family members.

Finding Role Models

As can be seen in our own wellness success stories, it is likely that most people have a story that makes them suitable wellness role models. Begin the search for people who have achieved the changer's wellness goal. Don't be discouraged if finding good role models requires some digging. These are private stories and it is frequently considered bragging to openly discuss successes. Although a couple of candidates could be enough, try to brainstorm and track down a larger list of candidates before settling upon your final choices. The following strategies are good ways to start.

- Look among family, coworkers, friends and acquaintances. Think about the various groups you belong to. Has anyone mentioned a similar wellness goal? These people are often open to a face-to-face discussion as well as follow-up support.

- Ask family, coworkers and friends if they know someone who has achieved a similar wellness goal. You may be pleasantly surprised about their contacts. A friend of a friend is often open to being of assistance.

- Find a local course or support group that focuses on your goal. The teacher or recent course graduates make knowledgeable role models. Many people continue to attend support group meetings well after they have achieved their goals. These people are often enthusiastic, willing to help and knowledgeable.

- A company wellness program coordinator or employee assistance program counselor may suggest some candidates who are willing to be contacted. Some helping professionals keep an active list of wellness role models.

✌ Chat rooms and discussion groups are now common on the Internet. These conversations often focus on wellness goals. You can find them at www.Google.com, or Groups. Yahoo.com. The participants in these discussions can be helpful role models.

✌ Personal stories, sometimes known as blogs, are now common on the Internet. An Internet search on a wellness goal may turn up one or more blogs created by potential role models.

✌ Associations have programs dedicated to wellness goals. Many of these groups are organized to address a disease. For example, the American Cancer Society has smoking cessation programs. The local chapters and the national organization will help identify possible role model candidates, suggest web resources, offer support groups and provide literature with success stories.

✌ Books, movies and self-help videos feature wellness success stories. Libraries, bookstores, DVD/video rental stores and online shops like Amazon.com are good sources. Many books in the medical and self-help section include personal testimonials. The authors frequently tell their own experiences to illustrate key concepts. Videos are now available on most wellness topics and feature eligible role models. The stories are often told in a compelling and entertaining format. The main disadvantage of these role models is that they tend to be inaccessible. It is unlikely that you will be able to establish an ongoing conversation with the creator of the content, but some will reference websites that support conversations with the author or with other readers.

Sizing-up Role Models

An effective role model provides inspiration, insight, encouragement and an appreciation of the many benefits of successful change. The following table describes key qualities both to cultivate and avoid.

Role Model Qualities

Qualities of an Effective Role Model	Qualities of an Ineffective Role Model
Has achieved similar goals under similar circumstances.	Has achieved a goal that differs in important ways. For example, an obese person's effort to lose 60 pounds is substantially different from an overweight person seeking to trim 5 pounds.
Recognizes that great benefits were realized through successful lifestyle change.	Views her own change efforts as more trouble than they were worth.
Willing to share his story, including the difficult parts.	Shares nothing about personal experience beyond that it was successful.
Willing to take time to tell her full story and to establish trust.	Not able/willing to share her experience and build trust.
Sees change as a process.	Expects quick fixes.
Is not quick to criticize or to judge.	Immediately makes character judgments.
Believes it is important to get support from others and shares how people played a role in success.	Thinks change is best achieved without the support or involvement of others.
Acknowledges that change can be a challenge.	Says that change is easy.
Gives permission to create own path to success.	Recognizes only one way to success: "my way."

Use this table of role model qualities to narrow down a list of possible role models to the best candidates. The table may also be helpful in conversations with a new role model. Sharing some of the qualities listed in the table will help clarify the type of support you are seeking. The qualities may also be useful later on. Use the list to see if you have gotten the full benefit of your relationship with a role model. For example, you may want to probe deeper for the challenges your role model experienced in achieving her goal.

Connecting with a Role Model

Asking someone to be a role model can be a tricky proposition. The term *role model* sometimes implies a level of perfection, and many people don't see themselves in this way. A good approach is for the changer to explain his wellness goal and to ask a role model candidate if she has achieved something similar. Follow-up questions could flesh out the role model's experience. At the end of the initial conversation, the changer can ask if it would be okay to ask follow-up questions as his efforts progress.

Questions for a Role Model

Have a set of questions ready before meeting with a role model. This will provide the most useful information and help keep the conversation flowing. The following questions are a good place to begin:

- What did you accomplish?

- What strategies did you use?

- How did you track your progress?

- What were some of the benefits of making the changes?

- What was particularly difficult and how did you overcome those challenges?

- What help did you get from others?

- Who inspired you or served as your role model?

- What sources of good information did you find?

- Can I check in with you after I begin to make my change?

Whenever possible, try to meet face-to-face with a role model. The in-person experience increases the level of communication, allows for personal warmth and enhances believability. Set aside adequate time so the conversation will not be rushed. Forty-five minutes to an hour usually works best.

Wellness Mentoring Stories

- At age 51, Raphael had a stroke. He had been really struggling to get on track both mentally and with his rehab program. His wife, Jana, asked a counselor for names of people who'd recovered from strokes. The counselor got permission from three of her prior clients to pass on their contact information. Raphael called a couple of the people focusing on the men, as he felt he could relate best to guys. The people he called were happy to share their experiences, but they turned out to be much older and well past retirement. Raphael felt that he should continue his search until he could find someone more like himself. They called the counselor for more names. Jana also purchased a book about stroke that included a number of success stories by younger men.

- Joanne is struggling with credit card debt. Her friend Jock wants to help. They decided to form a Wellness Mentoring relationship. Joanne and Jock warmed up to their discussion about finding a role model by sharing about past wellness successes. Joanne talked about her success in quitting smoking. Jock talked about his success in overcoming skin cancer. Jock had been fortunate enough to avoid credit problems himself and suggested that they look on the Internet for some leads. Jock identified some bloggers that have turned their debt problems around. Joanne is now exchanging email with one of these bloggers. Joanne and Jock decided to attend a seminar on debt problems. They asked the speaker to share success stories. They also asked to be put in touch with successful past participants.

- Steve is getting ready for the 160 kilometer Canadian Ski Marathon between Montreal and Ottawa, Canada. He knows that this will be a big athletic achievement so he contacted a good friend, Morgan. His friend had completed past ski marathons and offered to provide Wellness Mentoring support. They discussed role modeling. Morgan was glad to share his experience. He also knew a couple of other race veterans and was willing to introduce Steve by hosting a dinner party for them all. At the party, each was encouraged to share fun stories as well as their advice for completing the race. After the party, Steve developed a training schedule. He then ran it by several of his new friends.

- Ingrid had become concerned about global warming and wanted to change her life so that it would have less negative impact on the environment. She and her husband, Johannes, decided to use Wellness Mentoring to do this. When it came to the point of selecting role models, they decided to go to a meeting of activists. A number of helpful books were mentioned and a couple of the people talked about their own lifestyle changes. They stayed on after the meeting to mingle and exchanged numbers with other participants who were likely role models.

Identifying Role Models Checklist

Role models can be of immense inspiration. Role models can offer a beacon, a light at the end of the tunnel, as we embark on a lifestyle change. This means that it's well worth looking beyond immediate friends and family to find the best possible people to fill this role. The following checklist will help you determine whether you have addressed the potential for working with role models.

☐ We shared past health behavior change successes.

☐ We brainstormed sources of role model candidates and determined who will follow up and get contact information.

☐ We discussed role model qualities to get a clear picture of the desired characteristics.

☐ The changer has contacted candidates and begun the conversation with them.

☐ The changer has followed-up with role models to keep lines of communication and inspiration open.

Worksheet for Step 3

Wellness Mentoring Questions	Commentary
1. Exchanging Success Stories	
What are our past behavior change successes?	Exchanging success stories builds confidence. It also identifies skills and resources needed to achieve lasting and positive wellness goals.
2. Sizing-up Role Models	
What qualities are you looking for in an ideal role model?	Review the list of qualities of an effective role model and visualize the qualities desired.
What are the selection criteria for prioritizing the list of potential role models?	The criteria may help eliminate some candidates and help determine the most likely candidates.
3. Finding Role Models	
Who are the potential role model candidates?	Identify as many highly qualified and willing individuals.
4. Connecting with Role Models	
What is the plan for contacting potential role models?	Be sure to approach candidates in a friendly way that invites their assistance.
What questions will be asked of the role model?	Organize the interview in such a way that the role models will have an opportunity to share their stories and make useful suggestions.
What will be done to make it possible to pursue follow-up conversations?	Questions and tasks change throughout the behavior change process. Leave the door open for additional input from role models.

Step 4
Eliminating Barriers to Change

One of the greatest wellness stories of all time took place on Robin Island just off the coast of Capetown, South Africa. This was the site of a political prison that held Nelson Mandela and other South African leaders for several decades. The prisoners were held in small cells and allowed few privileges. Mandela and the other prisoners recognized that they would need their health if they were to survive and continue their work to end apartheid, so they committed themselves to doing everything within their power to sustain their mental and physical fitness. They exercised in their cramped cells and tried to eat as well as they could. They formed an underground school to sharpen their thinking and to sustain their mental health and well being.

By their final release in 1990, their discipline and creativity were so inspirational that it even moved their once-cruel prison guards to admiration and friendship.

Their story illustrates what can be done to pursue wellness even under the most oppressive conditions. Fortunately, few of us will ever endure the hardships experienced by Mandela and his fellow prisoners. While most of us experience barriers to wellness that are more of an inconvenience than a true hardship, the psychological and physical barriers we experience are *real*.

We often find that we lack the time, equipment and other resources needed to achieve wellness goals. We often find it difficult to justify our wellness activities. And many of us lack the discipline and focus to stick with a plan of action. To adequately address our barriers, we need help. Wellness Mentoring helps peers find ways over and around barriers to behavior change.

Determining Resource Needs

Successful behavior change frequently requires resources such as time, equipment and the cooperation of others. The following table can stimulate a discussion of the resources typically needed for such an effort.

Resources for Behavior Change

Resource Needs	Discussion
Time	Time is an important ingredient to success. Estimate how much time might be needed to achieve your wellness goal. For example, if physical activity is the goal, how much of your time will be spent exercising. Another aspect of time is making new behavior a regular or routine part of the day. Find a time when the needed energy levels and equipment are available, and also a time where competing commitments will not interfere with your behavioral goals.
Backing	We all juggle our responsibilities and commitments with others. Ideally, coworkers, supervisors, housemates and family will accommodate any shifts in responsibility needed to support your wellness goals. Determine who should be consulted and how to approach them. Determine how responsibilities such as childcare will be covered. If such accommodation is not available, how can these barriers be overcome or worked around?

Resources for Behavior Change (continued)

Resource Needs	Discussion
Equipment	Wellness activities require the right tools. For example, yoga routines benefit from loose-fitting clothes, a yoga mat and a quiet space with a comfortable temperature. In a similar way, a good garden plot and access to a health-oriented grocery store is important when the goal is to achieve a healthy diet. Determine any equipment that will be needed and how it will be found.
Expertise	Behavior change frequently requires know-how. It is much easier to stick with a behavior that you are good at and feel confident about. Formal training, mentoring and self-study can build knowledge, skill and confidence levels. Determine the best way to secure the information, practice and skills needed for success.
Focus	Mental health and a positive attitude are important factors in sustaining behavior change. For example, sleep is essential to a healthy attention span and other thinking processes. Anxiety can undermine focus. Mood also plays a role in achieving wellness goals. Fortunately many goals, such as exercise and healthy eating, enhance psychological well being. Determine how any unmet emotional and psychological needs may pose barriers. Make a plan for addressing those needs.

Conducting a Strength Review

Our strengths, not our weaknesses, help us move forward. Barriers can feel overwhelming when we lose track of our strengths. Forward momentum can be regained by conducting a strength review. Review resource needs and ask the following questions.

- **What resources are already available to you for achieving your goal?** Think about your strengths in terms of time, equipment, backing, expertise and focus. Come up with a comprehensive list.

- **How can your strengths be applied toward acquiring needed resources?** For example, a changer may have enthusiastic friends (a strength) willing to care for his children while he goes for a daily run.

Breaking Down Barriers

If requests don't work, some obstacles to wellness must be confronted head-on. If social pressures and a lack of resources are standing in the way of wellness, then it is not only appropriate, but also just, to demand that those barriers change. A society is in trouble when someone must be a hero or a martyr to do what's right.

Many support systems for wellness behavior are unfunded and under-resourced. So, for example, if there are too few bike lanes or paths, a changer interested in biking must join with others to demand that such wellness resources be built. If a changer cannot get healthy food at the grocery store, the changer and mentor need to ask that this deficiency be rectified. You can work with your peer to demand change. Here's how:

- ☞ **Discuss why wellness is a human right.** All people deserve good health and an opportunity to achieve their potential. People should be encouraged to pursue wellness goals, not discouraged. For example, the lack of whole-food restaurants or supermarkets and affordable fitness facilities undercuts wellness. Working long hours or foregoing vacations often seen as "necessary" in order to "get ahead" or 'succeed" also undermines wellness. Explore conditions that undermine growth, especially those related to the changer's goal. Discuss the role of society and social institutions in fostering wellness. Consider whether appropriate requests can be made of the workplace or community. While changes may not be made as quickly as you would like, you will be paving the way for others who follow you.

👍 **Develop strategies for working with gatekeepers such as a supervisor, coworker or housemate.** Asking for support frequently requires a game plan. For example, a work supervisor is more likely to extend the lunch hour to accommodate fitness, if the request is made respectfully, if the work still gets done, and if the supervisor understands the relationship between health and productivity. Take turns role playing such gatekeeper conversations.

👍 **Discuss what can be done to bring down wellness barriers.** Work rules and conditions, government service, laws and the activities of community groups can support wellness. There is some truth to the saying, "the squeaky wheel gets the grease." Ask for needed change. Join with others in advocating for needed organizational and community change.

Coping with Barriers

Behavior change is greatly facilitated when conditions are favorable. But, as was the case for the Robin Island inmates, wellness can be achieved even in the face of adversity. The following coping strategies may help you move through any apparent barriers.

👍 **Join with others.** You do not have to do this alone. As we will see in the chapter on supportive environments, support groups offer their members tremendous psychological strength and hope and encouragement.

👍 **Consult role models.** These people have likely experienced adversity and devised good coping strategies. Ask for their ideas and encouragement.

☝ **Change your focus.** A barrier does not negate the benefits of other available resources. Focus on what you want, your strengths and resources, and what can be accomplished. Make it a practice to review strengths and celebrate progress. Positive thoughts make struggle less taxing.

☝ **Be kind in other aspects of life.** Cut back on other responsibilities. Increase the amount of pleasurable activities in your day. Allow for renewal activities such as sleep, exercise and socializing with supportive friends.

☝ **Use any barriers to mobilize determination.** Barriers, especially when they are unkind, unjust or arbitrary can spawn outrage and resistance. Take a stand and resist. Don't let injustice and thoughtlessness win.

Wellness Mentoring Stories

- Angelo dreams of spending quality time with his wife and young daughter. His officemate, Larry, is working with Angelo to come up with a plan. The primary barriers are an unpredictable work schedule and Angelo's inability to communicate well with his boss (who is truly difficult to communicate with). Larry and Angelo talked about Angelo's current strengths. Angelo will try to parlay his record-breaking sales year into some time off and a fixed work schedule. He has practiced the conversation with Larry. Larry reminded Angelo to treat his boss with respect, but to remain firm about his needs.

- Jackie lives in rural Nebraska and manages her daily walk through November, but finds that the winter months are too dark and cold. She's also concerned about getting injured on the icy roads. Her friend Linda is trying to come up with a way to get through the winter with some kind of exercise program. They are planning on creating a community fitness room at the volunteer fire station.

- Art has arthritis. The pain keeps him from sleeping. His best friend Jim had focused on the arthritis but has decided to encourage Art to expand his research to include sleep issues. They talked about napping and about developing an evening routine that will promote good sleep. The nap requires a work break. Art would also need to get a couch for his office. Art and Jim role-played the conversation with Art's boss. Jim pretended to be Art's boss. Art was pleasantly surprised when his boss reversed his initial decision and agreed to let him take a nap in a conference room. He noticed that his Wellness Mentoring conversation with Jim had bolstered his confidence by enabling him to stick with his requests.

- Jan is training for the Lake Placid, New York, Ironman Triathlon but local traffic makes bike workouts scary. She talked with her mentor about her fears. They decided to attend a meeting of the local bike and pedestrian coalition. Since then Jan has become an advocate for bike lanes. She's written a letter to the editor, called the transportation department and brought her concerns to the town planner. She's been promised a bike lane by next year. It's too late for the Ironman training, but Jan's thrilled about her progress in creating a safer community.

Eliminating Barriers Checklist

Barriers can make wellness goals much more challenging to achieve. Addressing barriers requires creativity and good problem-solving skills. You are much more likely to come up with good strategies when you take time to approach resource needs together with a peer. The following checklist will help organize your efforts.

☐ We have a clear picture of the resources (time, backing, equipment, expertise and mental focus) that are needed to achieve wellness goals and any gaps in resources.

☐ We have reviewed existing resource strengths and how these may be applied to address barriers to change.

☐ We have requested or demanded needed resources.

☐ Where needed, we have engaged the support of gatekeepers such as supervisors, family members and housemates.

☐ Where needed, we have brought down barriers by effectively advocating for change.

☐ We have developed coping strategies for moving forward in spite of remaining barriers.

Worksheet for Step 4

Wellness Mentoring Questions	Commentary
1. Determining Resource Needs	
What time would help?	Although wellness goals for eliminating negative behavior may free up time, many positive practices, such as physical activity, require time for the new behavior. Ideally, this would be a predictable and regular time that allows for a routine.
What backing or permission would help?	Some goals require a release of responsibilities from other tasks such as work or childcare. Permission and cooperation can enhance what will be accomplished.
What equipment would help?	Some goals are best achieved with particular tools, clothes and other equipment.
What expertise would help?	Proper instructions and training make behavior change easier.
What mental health and attitude issues need to be addressed?	Lack of sleep, psychiatric conditions, anxiety and other mental factors can interfere with change. In contrast, a positive attitude and overall mental health make it more likely that goals can be maintained.

Worksheet for Step 4 (continued)

Wellness Mentoring Questions	Commentary
2. Conducting a Strength Review	
What resources are already available	Take stock of existing resources as such resources form a base upon which to work.
How can available resources be applied toward getting needed resources?	The people and places that already serve as resources are likely to offer clues about filling remaining gaps.
3. Breaking Down Barriers	
What is the justification for asking for resources to achieve our wellness goal?	Confidence that the goal is a good one and that it is worthy of needed resources is important to making the case for more resources.
Who will need to cooperate and how shall they be approached?	A strategy should be developed for asking for resources from gatekeepers such as supervisors and family members.
What will be done to tear down barriers?	Sometimes it is necessary to petition for changes in rules, lack of resources and other barriers. Such advocacy can be done solo and by joining with others.
4. Coping with Barriers	
What coping strategies will be used where resources are unavailable and barriers remain?	It is unlikely that change will occur under perfect conditions. Recognize the barriers and develop workarounds or coping strategies.

Step 5
Locating Supportive Environments

What comes to mind when you think of a supportive environment? Perhaps you're visualizing a tropical paradise or a gathering of smiling friends. A supportive environment does include special occasions and interesting places, but for our purposes right now, we're looking for something far less exotic. We're focusing on supportive daily environmental influences, like the people and the places in your daily routine.

The house, the workplace, the neighborhood and the grocery store are just some of the settings that influence your behavior. In a similar way, housemates, spouses, friends, children, coworkers, teammates, club members and neighbors form our immediate social – and hopefully supportive – circles.

Finding and creating physical, emotional and social environments that support wellness goals is an important Wellness Mentoring strategy. In this chapter I will share how you can bring environmental influences into focus, and how to modify these influences so that they better support desired wellness behavior. I will draw upon the perspectives of anthropologists, architects and city planners, who are all experts in understanding or creating environments.

Finding and Creating Supportive Physical Environments

When an architect plans a house, each room is designed to support its function. The kitchen has a stove, refrigerator, sink, cabinets and a countertop or a table. In a similar way, a behavior is easier to achieve with a supportive physical environment. For example, if healthy eating is the goal, access to attractive, nutritious and tasty foods is crucial. Grocery stores, restaurants and vending machines, should feature foods consistent with our goals.

Wellness Mentoring focuses on finding supportive places, limiting exposure to unsupportive environments and changing those aspects of our environments that work against wellness.

Think about where a new behavior is to happen. Is it

- Safe?

- Convenient?

- Well-maintained?

- A pleasant temperature?

- Appropriately equipped?

- Affordable?

- Comfortable?

Keep an eye out for unsupportive factors – the opposite of these. Some factors rank higher than others. For example, while Equinox Health Club in New York City meets all but one or two of these criteria, I rarely use it because I don't believe it is affordable for my short visits to New York and the club near our apartment doesn't have a lap pool.

What can be done to make the physical environment more supportive of wellness goals? Having assessed the physical environment, you and your peer can plan how to change recreational, work and living spaces so that they are more supportive. Consider finding new places. For example, early spring and late fall in Vermont are not conducive to outdoor exercise. A lucky few get out of state, but many migrate to health clubs and indoor skating rinks. We Vermont residents also set up treadmills and exercise bikes in our homes.

The following questions are useful for pursuing supportive physical environments.

- What places support your wellness goals and how can you spend more time in these places?

- What places are unsupportive, and how can they be changed or avoided?

- How can you find or create new supportive places?

Mobilizing Wellness Buddies

Many people find it easier and more enjoyable to do things with a companion. A wellness buddy is someone who has the same or a very similar wellness goal. It is like a buddy system for child safety at a pool. Both children swim and keep an eye out for one another. A wellness buddy may also be engaged in Wellness Mentoring, but this is not a requirement of a wellness buddy. Some peers assisting with Wellness Mentoring are serving solely as support people and are not engaged in behavior changes. The mentor might assist a peer with finding a wellness buddy.

The power of the wellness buddy approach has worked wonders in my life. Two days a week, I get together at 6 a.m. to jog with a couple of friends. On Sunday mornings I do my long run with a running club. During these jogs, we talk about current events, our lives and our exercise goals. These times with my wellness buddies are among my best. They keep me energized even though I'm not usually an early riser. My wellness buddies make my fitness routine truly enjoyable. We do this together.

Consider the following questions when establishing wellness buddy relationships.

- **Do my wellness goals lend themselves to partnering with another person?** Think creatively about this. Even activities that are generally done alone such as financial planning or managing an illness could be done more easily with another person who is pursing similar goals. Such people could be wellness buddies.

- **Who would make the best wellness buddies?** Existing social networks often offer good choices for wellness buddies. So if you were trying to manage weight, you could partner with housemates. Frequent contact and a shared refrigerator enhance the benefit. In addition to existing social networks, wellness buddies can be found in a support group, at a wellness seminar or on the Internet. Use the same approaches recommended in the Identifying Role Models chapter.

- **What are any barriers to finding wellness buddies?** In American culture there is a myth that the things we do by ourselves are somehow more enduring and superior than what we do with others. This has been a particularly strong message to men. We need to reach out to others even if it stretches us some. Once the ice is broken we usually find that the wellness-buddy approach is far superior to the go-it-alone approach.

- **What is the ideal schedule for connecting with wellness buddies?** This depends on the wellness goal. If the goal involves a routine, buddies can do that routine together. Weekly contact helps keeps the energy flowing. I joined Weight Watchers with my wife and neighbors. We attended weekly meetings together and then went out for sushi afterward to celebrate our progress.

Finding and Creating Supportive Cultural Environments

How would anthropologists rate someone's chances of achieving a wellness goal? They would look at the influence of tools, buildings and social networks. They would look to see if wellness behaviors get rewarded. They might also examine rites of passage, rituals and symbols – do they detract from or enhance wellness? So, if eating cake is the way people typically celebrate, they might suspect that losing weight will be difficult. Just like an anthropologist, you and your peer can examine your cultural environment to plan how to avoid unsupportive environments in favor of supportive cultural forces.

Some unhealthy aspects of our current cultures are hard to overlook. Such is the case with obvious excesses of a caffeine-drinking culture. American culture's problems with overeating are another example of a readily apparent health problem. When addressing cultural support, you and your peer will want to point out the unhealthy influences of the culture and develop strategies for reducing their impact. Wellness Mentoring works with three powerful, but too often overlooked cultural dimensions: cultural climate, cultural norms and cultural policies and procedures, which I refer to as touch points.

Fostering a Supportive Cultural Climate

When people don't get along, it is difficult to focus on personal growth. In a hostile environment people are angry, frustrated and uncooperative. In the United States, airports have come to symbolize such settings. The general buzz is predominantly negative and filled with suspicion. High security, overbooked flights and disgruntled airline employees keep people on edge. Other common examples of hostile or highly stressful environments are companies undergoing downsizing and families going through a divorce. Wellness Mentoring is directed at either resolving such conflict or finding ways to avoid the daily grind of unpleasantness.

A good climate takes different forms in households, workplaces and neighborhoods. Personal change is much easier in a friendly and cohesive social environment. In a marriage this might be referred to as the honeymoon phase. In a worksite it's called great teamwork. A strong sense of community, a shared vision and a positive outlook are dimensions of a supportive climate. These factors enhance individual and organizational growth. A sense of community provides for trust and openness. A shared vision enables people to be inspired by a common direction. A positive outlook makes it possible to use individual and collective strengths in meeting challenges. Finding or creating a healthy climate is a useful Wellness Mentoring skill.

You can examine the climate of your social environments with the *Cultural Climate Test.* The questions examine the three climatic dimensions.

Cultural Climate Test

Instructions: Focus on one of your social environments at a time. You can repeat the test for the important social groups in your life such as your household, work group, family and community organization. Rate your level of agreement with the following statements on the 5-point scale: (5) strongly agree, (4) agree, (3) undecided/don't know, (2) disagree, and (1) strongly disagree.

	Sense of Community
5 4 3 2 1	I know the people in my group really well.
5 4 3 2 1	I feel as if I belong here.
5 4 3 2 1	Members would support or care for me in a time of need.
5 4 3 2 1	I trust these people.
5 4 3 2 1	I feel comfortable saying what's on my mind.
	Shared Vision
5 4 3 2 1	We share common values.
5 4 3 2 1	I am able to explain the mission of my group.
5 4 3 2 1	I recognize how my own day-to-day activities contribute to the group's mission.
5 4 3 2 1	My group's conduct is consistent with its stated purpose and values.
5 4 3 2 1	My group has a clear and consistent direction.
5 4 3 2 1	Overall, I find my efforts with the group inspiring.

Cultural Climate Test (continued)	
	Positive Outlook
5 4 3 2 1	I am proud of the contribution my group is making.
5 4 3 2 1	My contribution to the group is recognized.
5 4 3 2 1	Achievements are celebrated.
5 4 3 2 1	We have a sense of humor about challenges we face.
5 4 3 2 1	We have a "can do" attitude.
5 4 3 2 1	Conflicts are resolved in positive ways.
5 4 3 2 1	Difficult assignments are treated as special challenges and opportunities, rather than problems.
5 4 3 2 1	I feel optimistic about the future of my group.

Scoring the Cultural Climate Test

The maximum score on the test is 95. Few groups achieve this ideal, but you and your peer can use the answers to identify ways to improve the climate. If most individual item scores are 3 or lower, consider limiting your exposure to this group.

With the help of the *Cultural Climate Test*, you can quickly understand the climate concept and how to assess the various social environments in your life such as your household, workplace, church or neighborhood. Then you can use these questions to develop a Wellness Mentoring strategy.

- **Do some of your social environments lack a supportive cultural climate?** If "yes," decide if it is likely to change, what you can do to turn it around and whether it is best to disengage. Focus on ways to minimize contact with hostile or toxic environments you can't change.

- **Do some of your environments provide a supportive cultural climate?** If "yes," how can you more fully benefit from them and how can people in this setting become involved in supporting your wellness goals.

- **How will you find settings with good climates?** Search for positive environments and ask an insider questions like whether people get along and if morale is good. Use the Cultural Climate Test questions as a guide in observing whether a sense of community, a shared vision and a positive outlook is evident. Some environments are difficult to read. In my neighborhood, for example, the annual summer picnic, beach cleanup and neighborhood meeting would be the only times to get a full read on the neighborhood's social climate. Until you have been at the picnic, you would not fully appreciate the positive spirit of the neighborhood.

Working with Cultural Norms

In a supportive culture, desired behavior is "the way we do things around here." People would be surprised if you behaved any other way. In a fitness-oriented household culture, for example, housemates would talk about their daily exercise plans and share responsibilities so that everyone gets time for physical activity. Housemates would share tips about running, biking and other interests. Fitness achievements would be celebrated.

Cultural norms are usually so embedded in the social fabric that we don't notice their influence. One quick test for a norm is to see if you get "pushback" from a group. If the behavior is against the norm, people are likely to get concerned about you and you are likely to hear statements like, "Around here, we don't do it that way." If it is a norm, the behavior will either meet with approval or go unnoticed. After all, "It is the way we do things around here."

Assess the norms in the changer's social environments to determine the level of cultural support for wellness goals. The following questions may help:

- Which social settings have norms that are for, neutral, or against the changer's wellness goal?

- How can you minimize exposure to groups with unsupportive norms?

- Which groups, if any, already have strong norms that support the changer's wellness goal?

- How can new groups with supportive norms be found or created?

- How can exposure to groups with supportive norms be maximized?

Working with Cultural Touch Points

A culture touches its members in subtle and not so subtle ways. If norms represent what is expected of people in a culture, touch points are the social mechanisms that establish and reinforce those expectations. Touch points, like reward systems, reinforce the behavior. Touch points are often embedded in formal and informal policies and procedures. For example, there may be a formal orientation program for a new employee offered by the human resources department and there is likely to be an informal orientation by coworkers that occurs on the job or over lunch.

In a family culture, most of the touch points are informal. For example, a family may discuss nutrition while at the grocery store or at the dinner table. This would be the informal communication system that influences goals for healthy eating. The following questions examine such cultural influences.

Examining Cultural Touch Points

Instructions: Focus on the changer's behavior change goal such as stopping drinking. Then answer the following questions to see how a group, family or organization hinders or promotes the desired wellness behavior.

Touch Points	Positive Influences	Negative Influences
Rewards and Recognition	Is the wellness behavior rewarded and praised?	Is undesired or unhealthy behavior rewarded and praised?
Modeling	Do leaders model the wellness behavior?	Do leaders model unhealthy behavior?
Confrontation	Is unhealthy behavior effectively discouraged or confronted?	Is the wellness behavior discouraged or ridiculed?
Relationships	Do people tend to form friendships while practicing the desired wellness behavior?	Do people form friendships around unhealthy practices?
Training	Do people get the training and skills needed to excel at the wellness behavior?	Are people taught skills that would make them more comfortable with unhealthy practices?
Orientation	Does the orientation (formal and informal) of new people give a first impression that the wellness behavior is the norm?	Are new people given the impression that unhealthy practices are acceptable?
Communication	Are people given feedback about how they are doing with the wellness behavior?	Would people be unlikely to have their wellness behavior noticed or assessed? Are such practices unmeasured and unreported?

Examining Cultural Touch Points (continued)		
Touch Points	**Positive Influences**	**Negative Influences**
Rites, Symbols and Rituals	Do celebrations, holidays and special events reflect support for the wellness behavior?	Do celebrations tend to feature unhealthy behavior?
Resource Commitment	Does the use of time, space or money show that the wellness behavior is important?	Are there inadequate resources available for the wellness behavior?

Many touch points work in unison to influence behavior. However, it is likely that some are giving contradictory messages. For example, a parent may communicate that she values healthy eating yet may be a poor role model when it comes to healthy eating. Other touch points may be sending no signals. For example, there may be no discussion of healthy eating in a family.

It takes power and influence to change touch points. If you do not have such authority, it is at least helpful to be aware of these influences and to advocate for needed change. If you have power, as is often the case of your family, a group of friends or with your immediate coworker, then work to adjust the touch points so that they better support wellness goals. The following ideas are often useful in thinking about adjusting cultural touch points.

- ♦ Many of these influences may have gone unexamined by group or organizational members. When these influences are revealed, members may be open to making changes.

- ♦ Efforts to change the influences frequently require decision-making authority or the support of those who have such authority. Try to get the power working for you.

✑ It is not necessary to create an entirely new system or to address all the negative influences. We are often better off making adjustments to existing influences.

✑ Start with the influences that will have the biggest impact and are easiest to change. For example, it may be easier to make changes with your work group or family culture.

Each of your cultural settings contributes to determining the *overall* influence. Each has its own touch points. For example, the workplace culture may offer predominantly positive influences; whereas the household culture may undermine wellness goals. Hopefully, the overall impact will be positive. However, it is likely that one or more settings will not fully support the wellness goal. As with negative norms and dysfunctional cultural climates, it is helpful to reduce contact with environments that have touch points that work against a wellness goal. Another tactic would be to increase contact with settings that are more likely to have a positive influence.

Wellness Mentoring Stories

- Joanne is using Wellness Mentoring to help her husband, Sam, get back on his feet after being laid off. Sam feels cut off and isolated. They discussed some possible wellness buddies. Sam was reluctant to connect with his former coworkers because they constantly complained about their old employer. Joanne suggested that Sam go down to the local office of employment and training. Sam called ahead and signed up for a seminar on interviewing. During the break, Sam met a couple of guys he liked. They decided to meet once a week over lunch and support each other in their job search.

- Angela was trying to cut back on her drinking, but her fights with Ramon really made it hard. Her best friend, Deb, using Wellness Mentoring, was helping. Deb asked about the cultural climate at home. Most conversations with Ramon quickly turned into shouting matches. Angela and Deb talked about the household climate and realized that something would have to change. Angela convinced Ramon to go with her to a counselor, and as they progressed, Angela also made progress with her drinking problem.

- Laura and her officemate, Derek, were obsessed with work and knew that this level of obsession was unhealthy. They were using Wellness Mentoring to help each other. Assessing the work climate, both immediately noticed that the norm was to work 60 or more hours a week. Many coworkers bragged about working though the weekend. Laura and Derek called a team meeting to discuss job burnout and the possibility of creating a healthier work culture. There was near universal agreement that the work culture had gotten out of hand. They discussed policies and procedures with their team. A number of policies were adopted including keeping track of work hours and setting the weekly individual limit to 50 hours. Laura and Derek were relieved that they would not have to make these changes alone.

- Crystal and Alice were partners. They had been together for 30 years and were both approaching retirement. They decided to use Wellness Mentoring to assist their planning process. Together, they listed environmental qualities they were seeking. They wanted a community that would be open to their lesbian relationship. Ideally, the setting would have norms for an active retirement. They wanted foreign language and yoga classes.

Locating Supportive Environments Checklist

Before turning to the next chapter on working through relapse, use the following checklist to determine if both mentor and changer have addressed important features of the environment.

☐ We have looked at physical environments and found ways to make them more supportive of wellness goals.

☐ We have explored the possibility of developing wellness buddy relationships.

☐ We have assessed the cultural climate and have found ways to limit contact with hostile or otherwise unsupportive environments. We will increase contact with settings with strong senses of community, shared visions and positive outlooks.

☐ We have identified cultural norms that support wellness goals. We have developed a strategy to become immersed in environments where our desired behaviors are "the way we do things around here."

☐ We have looked at cultural touch points embedded in formal and informal policies and procedures. We have found ways to increase desired influences and to lessen undesirable influences.

Worksheet for Step 5

Wellness Mentoring Questions	Commentary
1. Locating Supportive Physical Environments	
What is the ideal place and setup for your new behavior?	Think about a place that is safe, convenient, well-maintained, a desirable temperature, appropriately equipped, affordable and comfortable.
What places support the wellness goal and how can more time be spent in those places?	The right place makes wellness behavior easier.
What places are unsupportive and how can they be modified or avoided?	It is hard to continue do something if a space is not right.
How can you find or create new supportive places?	New surroundings offer an opportunity to pick places that are specifically chosen for their positive attributes.
2. Mobilizing Wellness Buddies	
Do your wellness goals lend themselves to partnering with another person?	If privacy is not a priority, then almost all wellness goals lend themselves to forming a wellness buddy relationship in which both people take on the same or similar goals together.
Who would make good wellness buddies	Start with existing social networks and housemates and, if necessary, look into support groups, wellness seminars and the Internet.

Worksheet for Step 5 (continued)

Wellness Mentoring Questions	Commentary
What are barriers to finding a wellness buddy?	Reach out to people to discuss wellness goals even if this means stretching the comfort zone. Role-play the conversation to get more comfortable. Most people are open to being asked.
What is the best schedule for connecting with wellness buddies?	Ideally the two wellness buddies will do some of their new behavior together, so coordinating such activities is important.
3. Locating Supportive Physical Environments	
What is the ideal place and setup for your new behavior?	Think about a place that is safe, convenient, well-maintained, a desirable temperature, appropriately equipped, affordable and comfortable.
What places support the wellness goal and how can more time be spent in those places?	The right place makes wellness behavior easier.
What places are unsupportive and how can they be modified or avoided?	It is hard to continue to do something if a space is not right.
How can you find or create new supportive places?	New surroundings offer an opportunity to pick places that are specifically chosen for their positive attributes.

Worksheet for Step 5 (continued)

Wellness Mentoring Questions	Commentary
3. Locating Supportive Cultural Environments	
What social settings, if any, have a hostile climate?	It will be important to spend less time in settings that lack a sense of community, a shared vision and a positive outlook as such settings sap energy and are distracting.
What social settings, if any, have cohesive climates?	It will be helpful to increase time in these settings as they enhance personal functioning and are good sources of social support.
What social settings have cultural norms that fail to support the wellness goal?	If a behavior is against the norm, it will be difficult to maintain. Contact with such settings should be limited.
What social settings have norms that support the wellness goal?	If desired behavior is also the norm, it will be easier to maintain that new behavior. Contact with such settings should be maximized.
What cultural touch points support the wellness goal?	It is helpful to take advantage of these touch points that may reward or otherwise endorse desired behavior.
What cultural touch points work against the wellness goal?	Strategies must be developed to reduce or work around these unsupportive influences.

Step 6
Working through Relapse

Wellness goals can be a great challenge. They involve changes in daily practices and sustained effort. They often require that we overcome ingrained habits, distractions, chemical addictions, and that we continue in spite of deep and long-standing psychological wounds. And, as we saw in the last chapter, we are likely to encounter many physical and social obstacles.

Given this, it is hardly surprising that most people do not achieve wellness goals on their first try. Some goals take many attempts before they are achieved. Those engaged in Wellness Mentoring must learn how to address the possibility of relapse and how people can move forward beyond the shame and doubt that often accompanies a setback.

Preventing Relapse

A great deal can be done to avoid relapse. Many of the best strategies have been described in previous chapters. We can avoid relapse by setting meaningful and achievable short- and long-term goals. We can visualize success and learn from the experience of role models. We can lower daily obstacles to change. We can find or create supportive social and physical environments. Together, these Wellness Mentoring strategies create assets that reduce the likelihood of relapse and failure.

Additional relapse-prevention approaches are aimed at avoiding high-risk situations. These questions can help you identify approaches to staying on track.

- **Are there places that should be avoided?** An alcoholic beginning recovery should stay away from bars. Identify the equivalent high-risk circumstance for the changer's wellness goal.

- **Are there social circumstances that should be avoided?** Maybe tensions at family gatherings make progress with overeating or stress management unlikely. Identify the groups and social activities that place the changer at risk.

- **Are there times of the day or week that are difficult?** For example, being tired often impairs judgment. Slow risers may find early morning a higher risk. Identify the times or days that may be challenging so strategies can be developed for working around the most vulnerable times.

- **Are there emotional states that are high risk?** Anger, sadness and fear often throw us off track. Identify the triggers for such emotions. Strategies for staying on track should be developed for these times.

Checking In

Schedule frequent meetings to discuss progress during the time the new wellness behavior is first being adopted. Lag time is an important factor in working though relapse. It is best to get back on track as soon as possible. So, for example, when I set a goal of cutting back on caffeine, I probably should have gotten some help soon after my first cappuccino. It was not long thereafter that I slipped back into my undesired practice throughout the day. I might have stuck with my goal if I had re-examined my commitment and approach right away with a supportive peer.

Even though relapse is common, it is best not to set an expectation for relapse. A discussion of how to address relapse should begin with the understanding that this is a "just in case" plan. Your hope is that relapse will be avoided and that progress will be steady.

Addressing a Relapse

Working through the emotional and physiological fallout of swings in wellness behavior requires great kindness, understanding, creativity and resilience. The following topics make it easier to address the "just in case" of relapse.

Restoring Adult-to-Adult Communication

Feelings of failure tend to make us feel small and guilty – more like a misbehaved child than an adult. And, just like a misbehaved child, there is a tendency to see others as parents – possibly angry or disappointed parents. This does not make for a good Wellness Mentoring relationship. We cannot be helpful or constructive in this parental role. No adult finds feeling like a misbehaved child satisfying. To manage these feelings, we avoid other people who treat us as children.

Wellness Mentoring requires getting back to a conversation between two equals – between two adults. The mentor can bring the relationship back to balance using the following strategies.

The mentor can:

1. Make clear that she is not a judge or a parent and that she sees the changer as an adult.

2. State that most people get off track, that she has on many an occasion, and that this is no big deal in terms of how she sees the changer.

3. Remind the changer that relapse is common. The mentor offers an example of how she has gotten off track during her own past behavior change attempts.

4. State that her respect does not depend on what the changer decides about the future effort.

5. State that her immediate goal is to find out what happened including the facts and the circumstances, and to determine – together – how to best move forward.

Interpreting Relapse

Listen for both facts and feelings. Was this a stumble or a true fall? A person thrown from a horse could get right back on the horse, decide to wait for a better horse, or decide that horseback riding is not such a great idea. What scenario fits best? Consider these choices:

✎ **Maybe this was a stumble and changer still sees himself as moving forward.** This would be a good interpretation of the experience as it maintains a sense of momentum. Perhaps there are some lessons that the stumble revealed about avoiding future troubles or about managing such incidents.

✎ **Maybe the changer views all momentum as lost and that it is necessary to start over.** If this is the case, the mentor should state his enthusiasm for a new beginning. Then he can see what adjustments in strategy and support may be helpful.

👍 **Maybe the changer wants to wait before starting over.** If this is the case, the mentor can acknowledge the decision and review some of the reasons for making the change with your peer. What would tip the balance toward making another go? What factors would determine when to make another attempt?

👍 **Maybe changer has had enough of this goal?** If this is the case, the mentor can acknowledge the decision and review possible alternative plans. What changes in goals and or strategy make sense? For example, if the changer is trying to address weight, he may want to change his goal from following a diet to physical activity. The mentor can offer assistance with any new goal.

Getting Out of a Funk

There is little doubt that a setback can be discouraging. Fortunately, Martin Seligman, Ph.D., a founder of the field of Positive Psychology, has developed a number of strategies for regaining our optimism. When we encounter a problem, we can choose to interpret that problem as a pessimist or as an optimist:

An Optimist's Interpretation	A Pessimist's Interpretation
My troubles are *not permanent*. It will soon go away.	My troubles are here to stay. I will always need to put up with this failing.
My troubles are *not pervasive*. This issue is limited in scope.	My troubles will ruin my entire life and spread over into other previously satisfactory things I have done.
My troubles are *not personal*. It is mostly caused by factors that are not my doing.	My troubles are my fault. I brought this upon myself and no one and nothing else is to blame.

Moving toward the optimist's position is a useful strategy for raising your spirits after a slip or relapse. Examine the situation to look for reasons why the relapse is not permanent, not pervasive and not personal. The strategy only works if you believe it is truth. Look for credible reasons why you can take the position of the optimist.

Fortunately, as we have seen throughout *Not Alone*, there are many external factors that help determine behavior change outcomes. They are at least partially responsible for any relapse. And, as we learned in the *Call to Action*, it often takes many tries before people succeed.

Unhealthy behaviors don't have to be permanent. The new positive interpretation of the event can lift the cloud of failure and bring new light on the situation.

Wellness Mentoring Stories

- Vince is using Wellness Mentoring to help his friend Dave break his drug addiction. They discussed the possibility of relapse, and Dave acknowledged that he had been fighting his addiction unsuccessfully for more than 10 years. They discussed those "learning experiences" with an eye toward improving the chances of success. Dave was convinced that strides in establishing new physical and social surroundings were going to be a big help. Dave was going to make a special effort not to hang out with anyone who had a drug problem. He was also going to avoid alcohol over the holidays and stay away from those places and parties where he knew he would be pressured to drink. Vince and Dave agreed that, no matter what happened, they would remain friends and maintain an adult-to-adult relationship. For the time being, they would check-in with each other daily.

- June had set some big goals for diet and exercise after her heart attack. She had befriended another survivor, Arlene, in the cardiac rehabilitation program, and they were using *Not Alone* together. June had a rough time sticking with her exercise routine. Arlene knew there was something up because June was hesitant to talk about her progress. It was getting awkward and Arlene decided to clear the air by sharing her hunch. June readily shared her frustrations and the two had a laugh over how June's husband behaved when she put on her workout clothes. They talked more seriously about resetting goals to make them more doable. They also talked about getting June's husband on board.

- Lauren and Clay have a three-year-old daughter. They were both frustrated at the drop off in their sex lives. They were using Wellness Mentoring to make a change. The first thing they agreed about was that it was not easy to balance work and family responsibilities. They were having a hard time coming up with a time when they both had the energy for sex. Juggling new parenting responsibilities seemed like a higher priority. They agreed to be patient and focus initially on getting some fun time together as a couple. To that end, they found a babysitter and declared that Tuesday would be date night. Their wellness goal had changed, but they felt hopeful about their future together.

Working through Relapse Checklist

Before turning to the next chapter on celebrating success, see if you have planned for possible relapse. The following checklist helps determine if you have covered the important aspects.

☐ We developed ways to avoid situations that may trigger a relapse.

☐ We set check-in times so that setbacks can be discussed soon after they first appear.

☐ We affirmed our goal of maintaining an equal adult-to-adult relationship regardless of how or whether wellness goals are achieved.

☐ We explored the range of possible setbacks and recognized that we can move forward after a relapse.

Worksheet for Step 6

Wellness Mentoring Questions	Commentary
1. Preventing Relapse	
What social situations should be avoided?	Some people and social events are triggers for the old behavior. They raise the risk of relapse and should be avoided.
What places should be avoided?	Some places trigger old and unwanted behavior. They raise the risk of relapse and should be avoided.
What times of the day or week are particularly difficult and what can be done to pay special attention during these times?	Coping methods can be used to make it easier to get through those times when the old behavior is most tempting.
What emotional states are high risk and how can they be avoided?	Sadness, anger, frustration, fatigue, drinking alcohol and other emotions can throw us off. Efforts should be made to limit such mental states and to develop coping strategies.
2. Checking In	
How often will the changer and mentor check in so that relapse can be discussed early on?	It is important to stay in touch to offer encouragement and to address relapse issues?

Worksheet for Step 6 (continued)

Wellness Mentoring Questions	Commentary
3. Addressing a Relapse	
How will we make sure that we return to adult-to-adult communication?	When a relapse occurs, it is common to feel like a misbehaving child. It is important to quickly return to feeling like an adult.
What is the result of a relapse in terms of next steps?	Determine if: (1) the goal has been abandoned, (2) a decision made to start over, or (3) a temporary stumble occurred.
How will we regain optimism and get out of a funk?	A relapse can be less draining if interpreted as temporary, narrow in its impact, and not entirely the fault of the person who has relapsed.

Step 7
Celebrating Success

Too often, successes go unacknowledged. Unheralded success does more than undercut our good cheer. It is a missed opportunity to reinforce desired practices. This is particularly true with wellness goals in American culture as daily practices are considered private endeavors and sharing progress is called bragging.

An unintended side-effect of the "go it alone" approach is that no one even knows when benchmarks are set, let alone achieved. In the health care setting, for example, privacy agreements forbid sharing, even when it's good news.

Advocates of the quiet approach go on to praise the value of self-achievement and self-responsibility as if help from others somehow taints successful behavior change and downgrades the achievement. "She did it entirely on her own," becomes special bragging rights. I have come to understand, however, that often, when someone "does it on her own," it is a sad sign of a disconnected society and a strong indication that the changes will be short lived. We want and need to celebrate together.

Celebrating All Along the Way

One of the best things about Wellness Mentoring is that we actively seek opportunities to celebrate – and there are many to be found. This goes well beyond the typical approach of celebrating only when the ultimate goal is achieved. Consider the possibilities for celebrating success.

You celebrate when:

- ✋ You complete the Wellness Behavior Profile and determine that you already had many great wellness strengths.

- ✋ You set a wellness goal.

- ✋ You find a role model.

- ✋ You get input from your role model. This is also an opportunity to appreciate the role model's input.

- ✋ You eliminate one or more barriers to change.

- ✋ You find people and places that will support your wellness goal.

- ✋ You develop strategies for limiting contact with unsupportive environments.

- ✋ You develop and implement strategies for avoiding relapse.

- ✋ You get back on track after a relapse.

- ✋ It is the anniversary of a significant achievement.

In addition to this list, there are times to celebrate that correspond to the stages of behavior change discussed in the *Not Alone* chapter on goal setting. Each stage has its own transition and marker. These should be celebrated. The following table describes these changes in broad terms.

Transitions Included in Prochaska's Stages of Behavior Change

Transition	Marker
From Developing Commitment to Preparation	Date set for making the change.
From Preparation to Action	Personal changes begun.
From Action to Maintenance	Early adjustment shifts to long-term sustainability.
From Maintenance to Moving On	New lifestyle is completely comfortable–ready to move on to other goals.

Dividing up behavior change by stages offers several opportunities to celebrate. When we move from thinking about change to setting a time to make that change, it is time to celebrate. When we have finished preparing and begin to make the behavior change, we can celebrate again. Celebrations are also in order when behavior changes have been successful for a short period. When changes have taken hold several months or a year into it is one more time to celebrate.

Tuning in with Intrinsic Rewards

Good celebrations often include rewards. Such rewards come in two forms: **intrinsic** and **extrinsic**. An intrinsic reward is a benefit that directly results from behavior change, for example, feeling more energetic after becoming fit. An extrinsic reward is a benefit from another source. The 30-day sobriety chip of Alcoholics Anonymous would be an example of an extrinsic reward.

Most wellness goals result in multiple intrinsic rewards. Someone with a wellness goal for addressing breast cancer might gain an intrinsic reward of being free of cancer signs and symptoms. She might also learn how to manage great personal threats and challenges. The process and achievements may have proven to be a great source of self-discovery and an opportunity to establish new personal priorities. These would all be intrinsic rewards.

Explore the intrinsic rewards likely to result from the changer's efforts and ultimate goal achievement. What are all the intrinsic benefits? Achieving wellness goals lowers the probability of getting sick and reduces recovery time. In addition, many wellness-related behavior changes improve job performance and mood. Sometimes our wellness achievements directly benefit those we love. Stopping smoking, for example, improves health outcomes for our children.

Some benefits are surprising. Did you know that stopping smoking improves sexual performance? There is a lot of scientific information about the various health consequences associated with unhealthy and healthy behavior. You and your peer can review this information to uncover some wonderful rewards.

Looking for a Longer Life

Some practices mean the difference between life and death. Perhaps your peer has set a wellness goal that could enhance her life expectancy. The likelihood of a longer life is a powerful intrinsic reward. The likelihood this promise is being kept can be assessed through a self-test called a health risk appraisal. This test uses life expectancy or actuarial tables generated by health researchers and life insurance companies to predict how long people live. It shows the link between behavior and how long you are likely to live. By modifying risk, you can increase your likelihood of living longer.

To see how this works, you can complete and share the following Life Expectancy Test with your peer. The Life Expectancy Test first appeared in my dad's 1977 book, *Lifegain*, and has been reprinted in *Time* and dozens of other publications. The beauty of the test is that it is self-scoring and it offers feedback about the impact of behavior on life expectancy. However, there are far more scientific and current tests available (see www.realage.com for a free online test).

Life Expectancy Test

More than half of our life expectancy is determined by lifestyle factors such as diet, exercise and smoking. Other factors, such as heredity, quality of medical care and the physical environment, also play roles in life expectancy. To see how this works in your life, answer the following questions. They are based on government and insurance company research on how long people live.

	Life Expectancy Factor	Running Total
	Start with the number 76.	76
	Age adjustment: If you are under 30, add nothing. Between age 30 and 40, add 2. Between age 40 and 50, add 3. Between age 50 and 70, add 4. Over age 70, add 5.	
	If you are male, subtract 7.	
	If you live in an urban area with a population over 2 million, subtract 2.	
*	If you live in a town of under 10,000 or on a farm, add 2.	
	If a grandparent lived to 85, add 2.	
	If all four grandparents lived to 80, add another 6.	
	If either parent died of a stroke or heart attack before the age of 50, subtract 4.	
	If any parent, brother, or sister under 50 has (or had) cancer, or a heart condition, or has had diabetes since childhood, subtract 3.	
	If you live with a spouse or friend, add 5.	
*	Subtract 1 for every 10 years you've lived alone since age 25.	
*	If you finished college, add 1.	
*	If you have a graduate or professional degree, add another 2.	

Life Expectancy Test (continued)		Running Total
	Life Expectancy Factor	
*	If your job pays over $100,000 a year, subtract 2 for accompanying stress.	
*	If you are 65 or over and still working, add 3.	
*	If you work behind a desk, subtract 3.	
*	If your work requires regular, heavy physical labor, add 3.	
*	If you exercise strenuously (tennis, running, swimming, etc.) five times a week for at least a half-hour, add 4. Two or three times a week, add 2.	
*	If you are overweight by 50 pounds or more, subtract 8. By 30 to 49 pounds, subtract 4. By 10 to 29 pounds, subtract 2.	
*	If you sleep more than 10 hours each night, subtract 4.	
*	If you are intense, aggressive, or easily angered, subtract 3.	
*	If you are easygoing and relaxed, add 3.	
*	If you are happy, add 1. Unhappy, subtract 2.	
*	If you have had a speeding ticket in the last year, subtract 1.	
*	If you smoke more than two packs a day, subtract 8. One or two packs, subtract 6. One-half to one, subtract 3.	
*	If you drink the equivalent of a pint bottle of liquor (or a bottle of wine) a day, subtract 1.	
*	If you are a man over 40 and have annual checkups, add 2.	
*	If you are a woman and see a gynecologist once a year, add 2.	
	Total	

Your total is your likely life expectancy age. If you would like to increase your life expectancy, look back over the questions that begin with an asterisk and find those in which you subtracted years or were unable to add years. Change those to positive health practices and you improve your chances for a longer life.

Do your wellness goals enhance life expectancy? Don't be discouraged if your goal is not on the Life Expectancy Test. This is a rough estimate and there are many additional practices that have proven to be important in health and longevity. If, however, your goals offer hope for a longer life, you should share the news of this additional intrinsic reward with your peer.

Getting Rewarded by Others

Extrinsic rewards are the way peers, groups and society reinforce wellness. For example, your peer could reward you with praise, a card or some other form of acknowledgment. Similar informal rewards are available from other peers such as family, friends and housemates. For example, a man who has lowered his cholesterol might comment that one great reward was the look on his wife's face when the results came back.

Organizations and society also have rewards for wellness activities such as incentives for completing company health risk appraisals. Good health could lead to job promotions, since advancement is often linked to personal productivity and we tend to be a lot less productive or absent from work when we are sick. There are also rewards associated with competitions. I appreciate the T-shirts and medals I get for competing in fitness events.

Sometimes extrinsic rewards are criticized because they are considered a distraction from intrinsic rewards. Other criticisms concern how external rewards are often temporary and they are not controlled by the person making the change. It does at first appear odd to pay someone for doing something that offers great intrinsic health benefits. However, in most cases it is best to have a powerful mix of both intrinsic and extrinsic rewards. For example, stopping smoking is a great accomplishment with direct intrinsic health benefits for those who quit. However, external rewards, such as lowered health insurance deductibles for non-smokers, do not undermine the intrinsic rewards. External rewards just make the behavior change even more rewarding and are likely to get the attention of those who have yet to pay attention to the intrinsic rewards.

With Wellness Mentoring we are going to tune in to the intrinsic health and self-esteem rewards *and* make sure that our peers get all the external perks, pay and praise available for their achievements.

Refining the Reward Systems

As can be seen with the list of reasons to celebrate and with the variety of intrinsic and extrinsic rewards available, there are many ways to make celebrations meaningful and appropriate. The following questions can assist with tailoring celebrations to best suit your needs.

When we celebrate:

- **What are the desired levels of privacy and how will they be maintained?** As a general rule, public disclosure and commitment work in favor of successful behavior change. It is a lot harder to give up or go back once you have declared your intentions and progress. However, the changer may not want particular people to know about any changes under way. Who should and should not know? How can we celebrate and yet maintain desired confidentiality?

- **How can we make rewards compatible with wellness?**
  In American culture many common rewards are
  inconsistent with a wellness message. For example, a
  piece of cake is not an appropriate extrinsic reward
  for successful weight management. Exotic fruits and
  vegetables make a good alternative. A new outfit
  could be a more fitting reward. We must often be
  creative and willing to break with tradition to create a
  wellness reward system.

- **Are there savings that can be applied toward financing
  a grand prize?** When I stopped drinking diet soda
  and fancy coffees, I put the money into a travel fund.
  In the course of a couple of years, these savings made
  it possible for me to take my grandmother on a cruise
  to Alaska. See if your achievements offer some savings
  or another financial benefit. Avoiding illness adds to
  productivity and reduces costs. Can some or all of this
  money be redirected toward a fitting reward?

- **What are your favorite ways to celebrate?** We all have
  our preferences – our favorite way to relax, our favorite
  healthy foods, our favorite way to exercise, our favorite
  places. Rewards should be tailored to personal taste.
  What is the nicest thing anyone ever said to you? Maybe
  the tone and spirit of that comment can be mirrored in
  how wellness achievements are celebrated. For example,
  I particularly found it satisfying when my father talked
  to me in private about how proud he was of my professional achievements. I favor similar private acknowledg-
  ments of current wellness achievements. Some people
  find monetary rewards most meaningful. If this is the
  case, a good celebration includes cash or a check.

- **Are there special celebrants?** Perhaps certain esteemed friends, family members or coworkers would offer particularly meaningful rewards – intrinsic or otherwise. Expressions of delight from a spouse, an "atta boy" from the boss, or praise from mom and dad may carry special weight.

Talk about some of the rewards that would be meaningful with your peer. It is sometimes necessary to apply for rewards. The classic example is when we make a wish list for holiday presents. With wellness achievements, for example, it might be necessary to bring our good health and productivity to the attention of our supervisor and alert her about our desire for a promotion. In a similar way, if acknowledgment from our spouse would make a good reward, then he would need to know about progress and be keyed-in about the hoped-for praise.

Finishing Strong

If you have organized your efforts in the same sequence as in this book, then you may be reaching a good check-in point for your wellness efforts. Presumably you and your peer have discussed and worked with the six primary Wellness Mentoring strategies of goal setting, identifying role models, eliminating barriers to change, locating supportive environments, working through relapse and, with this chapter, celebrating success.

Take stock of your relationship:

👍 Spend a few moments in appreciation of your time together, the trust you have maintained, your commitment to success and your ability to adapt.

⚘ Discuss what each of you has learned in terms of peer support and how best to approach behavior change in the future.

⚘ Decide how you will work together in the future. Include in this conversation any new goals that should be considered, time commitments and any other adjustments. For example, you may decide that by a certain date it would be a good time to meet less frequently, or to move to more of a check-in format with telephone calls and emails.

⚘ Find some way to celebrate your relationship. This celebration could take the form of a symbol of your appreciation or a special meal or a shared fun event.

Wellness Mentoring Stories

- José and his wife, Rita, are using Wellness Mentoring to achieve environmental goals for energy conservation. They have adjusted their thermostats and reorganized their work so they can commute two days a week by public transportation. They are tracking their heating bill and travel costs. Half of their savings will go to environmental causes and the rest will be spent on a bike trip across their state.

- Stan has set a wellness goal for spending more time with his son. His friend and coworker Dave is using Wellness Mentoring to assist. Stan had been thinking about making this change for the past six months and has set New Year's Day for putting his plan into action. Dave offered to take Stan and his son out to celebrate Stan's commitment. The three whooped it up at a local college basketball game.

- Ernie and his cousin Paula stopped smoking a year ago on April 5. Another family member, Clair, used Wellness Mentoring to support their efforts. Clair put together a surprise party for the anniversary. More than 20 family members sang an adaptation of "Puff the Magic Dragon" at the big event.

- Emina has been helping Jen with her weight. They talked about progress. The conversation turned to some of the rewards she could anticipate. Jen was looking forward to climbing stairs without losing her breath. Jen also knew that her weight had become an issue at work, where she was required to do a lot of walking. She worried about what all the walking was doing to her knees. Emina asked if there were any additional rewards that might be fun. Jen's eyes brightened as she said, "I could buy a new wardrobe."

Celebrating Success Checklist

See if you have a good plan for celebrating success. The following checklist helps determine if you have covered the important aspects.

☐ We have identified several times in which to celebrate when plans are made and when goals are achieved.

☐ We have compiled a comprehensive list of intrinsic rewards (such as health and well being benefits) that are likely to occur if we are successful.

☐ We have identified extrinsic rewards (such as pay, bonuses and gifts) that will be available as a result of the wellness effort.

☐ We have discussed strategies for tailoring celebrations and rewards so they are appropriate and meaningful.

☐ We have celebrated our relationship by checking in and by honoring our time together.

Worksheet for Step 7

Wellness Mentoring Questions	Commentary
1. Celebrating All Along the Way	
Have we identified several reasons to celebrate?	Many successes go unacknowledged, which undermines positive energy. It is important to look for the many opportunities to acknowledge wellness efforts.
What are the markers for the transitions in the stages of behavior change and how will these transitions be recognized and acknowledged?	The six stages of behavior change offer a roadmap for focusing efforts, and moving one stage forward deserves a celebration.
2. Tuning In with Intrinsic Rewards	
What are the health and quality-of-life rewards for achieving the changer's wellness goal?	Such benefits include feeling more energetic, increasing personal performance, reducing a health risk, healing and living longer, Some benefits will readily be felt while others may require a review of the scientific literature.
How might success with the goal benefit others?	Many wellness goals benefit others. This benefit may be important to the changer. For example, when someone quits smoking, it may improve the air quality of family members and lesson the likelihood that children will smoke.

Worksheet for Step 7 (continued)

Wellness Mentoring Questions	Commentary
3. Getting Rewarded by Others	
How will successful behavior change be acknowledged?	Lowered health risk and positive practices sometimes trigger rewards such as lower insurance premiums, financial savings, praise and other forms of extrinsic rewards. It is sometimes necessary to apply for such payoffs.
4. Refining the Reward System	
What degree of privacy is desired with rewards?	Some people are less comfortable with public acknowledgment so their rewards need to be low key.
How will rewards be made compatible with wellness?	Standard rewards may be inconsistent with a wellness message, so it is often necessary to create more healthful strategies.
Are there financial savings that will result from the behavior change and can this money be incorporated into a reward?	The savings are easy to see if the old practice cost money, but other savings of time, fewer absences and reduced health care costs can also be factored in.
Are there special celebrants who should be involved with the rewards for achieving wellness goals?	Family members, friends and mentors could add meaning to rewards by being involved with acknowledgment of change.

Worksheet for Step 7 (continued)

Wellness Mentoring Questions	Commentary
5. Finishing Strong	
What has been useful and enjoyable about the Wellness Mentoring relationship?	Reflect on the positive qualities of the relationship, how it evolved, how challenges were overcome and what was accomplished.
How will the Wellness Mentoring relationship be acknowledged?	Celebrate the relationship and how it has enriched the lives of the changer and mentor.

Bringing On the Wellness Revolution

Congratulations! You are now familiar with the principles and techniques of effective peer support. This final chapter explores the potential role of peer support in advancing wellness. The chapte also explores the broad social implications of mobilizing peer support to bring on a wellness revolution.

Wellness is truly a revolutionary vision that holds great promise for prevention, healing, peak performance and improved quality of life. Being part of the wellness revolution requires making changes in the way we live. Physical activity, good nutrition, adequate sleep, stress reduction and the avoidance of substance abuse play important roles in wellness. Healthy social connections are another part of the wellness revolution. These connections begin in the uterus and extend to how we leave the world for future generations.

Wellness Mentoring weaves together both the wellness domains of personal behavior and social connection. By enhancing the quality and quantity of social support, Wellness Mentoring increases the likelihood of success. Furthermore, efforts to offer effective support enhance human connections. Helping people with behavior change has been primarily the domain of the therapist and wellness professional. Extending this helping role to our peers can bring on a wellness revolution.

Curing the Epidemic

Wellness Mentoring can help cure the epidemic of destructive health practices in North America and in many other parts of the world. The number of Americans who adhere to all four of the most basic lifestyle prescriptions for health – not smoking, maintaining a healthy weight, eating adequate fruits and vegetables, and exercising regularly – is a dismal 3 percent, according to a 2005 study of 150,000 adults. Steven Aldana, author of *The Culprit And the Cure,* tells a tragic story of an America caught in the grips of a spiraling epidemic of widespread unnecessary suffering and premature death.

The following facts from *The Culprit & the Cure* show why it is so important that we begin to change our health behaviors.

- Consider some of the recent findings for the United States.

  — 1 out of 4 adults smoke

  — 2 out of 3 adults are overweight or obese

  — 3 out of 4 adults don't get enough exercise

  — 4 out of 5 adults eat an inadequate diet

- Americans are losing ground even among children. Over the past 40 years, the number of American children who are overweight quadrupled. Physical inactivity is also on the rise. The projections are for widespread diabetes among children.

Research findings regularly report the benefits of a wellness lifestyle. For example, a California study determined that if you exercise regularly, do not smoke, and get adequate sleep, your death rate due to cancer and cardiovascular disease is 70 to 80 percent lower than the rest of the nation. The impact of this short list of health practices on life expectancy is staggering. Males with these health practices live an average of 11 years longer and females live an average of seven years longer than average Americans. Research has also found that a person adopting healthy practices is not only more likely to avoid chronic conditions, but the final years are more apt to be healthier ones.

In contrast with the benefits of a wellness lifestyle, the dire consequences of unhealthy behavior are compelling. Once you appreciate the connection between unhealthy practices and poor health, the economic consequences of the epidemic become obvious. Poor health undermines productivity. You can't work as well when you are sick. Poor health requires a lifetime of expensive and otherwise unneeded medical care. To cut the risks of catastrophic illnesses, health professionals are performing surgeries and prescribing drugs to address health issues that are best treated with behavior changes such as a healthy diet and exercise.

Cleaning the Poisoned Cultural Well

Most epidemics can be traced to a source. The classic public health example is a poisoned well in London. The people in the vicinity of the Broad Street pump were getting sick. John Snow figured this out and removed the pump's handle and the illness vanished.

In the case of unhealthy behavior, cultural environments are the most likely source. The culture is the poisoned well. Smokers learn to smoke through movies, their family and friends. Television and computer games, primary ingredients for couch potatoes, are social inventions. Bars, parties and alcohol ads have their role in making people susceptible to substance abuse.

Given the many negative influences in North American culture, it is tempting to tell people to go it alone – it's just too hard to get support to do what you want to do. But, just as the residents of London could not do without another source of water, humans require social contact to survive and thrive. Healthy practices can have social roots. Those who exercise regularly, for example, probably learned and were encouraged in developing their fitness skills through a coach, family member or friend. The question is not really whether we will have social contact, but rather whether this contact supports our wellness.

As was pointed out in the chapter on *Locating Supportive Environments,* we can help each other achieve health behavior goals by finding supportive wellness buddies, changing cultural norms and organizational policies and creating cohesive social climates. With Wellness Mentoring strategies such as these, we can begin to clean the poison from the well of unsupportive cultures at home, at work and in the community. *Locating Supportive Environments* begins a conversation about cultural change. You can further explore this important subject at www.healthyculture.com The website features surveys, training and publications about cultural change.

Connecting

Throughout this book, I have explained how people can help each other achieve wellness goals. Using Wellness Mentoring techniques, you and your peers can make dramatic and lasting behavior changes. Together, you can achieve success rates that would not be possible without support.

If this book has any role in your success, then it was well worth the writing. But the very act of people coming together has a benefit that may far exceed the health benefits and personal satisfaction that we have described. There is strong evidence that human connection is, in and of itself, as powerful a positive life force as any health behavior change. The very act of reaching out to help someone in constructive ways enhances your own health and the health of your peers. And the connections you are making enhance the well being of your workplace, your community, your country and the planet.

Promoting Health with Human Interaction

Cardiologist Dean Ornish's book *Love And Survival* is a masterful summary of research on the health benefits of human connections. Dr. Ornish cites over 100 studies that make a compelling case that love, intimacy and human connections prevent illness, heal disease and extend life. The following quote summarizes Dr. Ornish's findings:

- Do you have anyone who really cares for you? Who feels close to you? Who loves you? Who wants to help you? In whom you can confide?

- If the answers are "no," you may have a *three to five times* higher risk of premature death and disease from all causes – or even higher, according to some studies. These include increased risk of heart attack, stroke, infectious disease, many types of cancer, allergies, arthritis, tuberculosis, autoimmune diseases, low birth weight and low Apgar scores, alcoholism, drug abuse, suicide and so on. This reduction in premature death was found in people who were healthy and in those who were unhealthy at the start of these studies. Also people are much more likely to choose life-enhancing behaviors rather than self-destructive ones when they feel loved and cared for.

There is parallel evidence that the health benefits of human connection accrue to those providing support. In one study of more than 700 elderly adults, the more love and support they offered, the more they benefited themselves. Just as with this population of elders, offering Wellness Mentoring has direct health benefits to the mentor. Such support reinforces the mentor's own positive health practices. And it is harder for us to advocate something for someone else while continuing a contradictory behavior ourselves. In addition, as we help others with behavior change, we learn and reinforce skills useful for achieving our own wellness goals. When we help our peers adopt healthier practices, we create a peer culture that is more supportive of our own wellness.

Succeeding at Work

How do you gauge success at work? Your list might include a good salary, a boss who gives you the freedom and support to innovate and do your job well, friendly and mutually supportive coworker relationships, decent work hours, good benefits and job security. Although the quality of your workplace depends on a variety of market forces, government regulations and other external factors, constructive social relationships play an important role in your success as an employee or employer. *In Good Company*, a book out of the Harvard Business School, describes the role of social relationships in business success. The authors, like many economists, consultants and sociologists, define positive relationships as social capital:

> *Social capital* consists of the stock of active connections among people: the trust, mutual understanding, and shared values and behaviors that bind the members of human networks and communities and make cooperative action possible.

In Good Company reviews many research findings and case studies that link social capital and positive business outcomes. With good social relationships, workers find it easier to voice their concerns and to join with others to have them addressed. Trust and openness make relationships with customers less problematic and legalistic. Good social relationships give people the space, time and constructive feedback needed to innovate. Collaboration and teamwork make it more likely that people will follow through on commitments. In addition, social capital increases morale and job retention. The end result is that good social relationships make work more enjoyable and profitable for all concerned.

In the chapter *Locating Supportive Environments*, I focused on a specific aspect of social capital – social climate. We saw how a supportive social climate makes it easier for people to change their behaviors. Our assignment was to examine the social climate and to limit contact with those environments that lack a sense of community, a shared vision and a positive outlook. We saw the importance of seeking out and spending more time in groups and settings that have these climatic factors.

But Wellness Mentoring has an impact on social capital that goes beyond boycotting some settings and seeking out others. Wellness Mentoring plays a constructive role in generating good work relationships. When it is applied in a work setting, social capital rises. Here's how:

 🖎 Wellness Mentoring provides employees with a way to help one another and to build mutual trust. Participants learn more about each other – beyond job functions. This broader relationship provides for better communication and trust. The camaraderie associated with taking on big lifestyle challenges carries over into other work functions. Wellness Mentoring is like a ropes course or an adventure retreat in that personal risk is paired with the enthusiasm and support of coworkers.

 🖎 Wellness Mentoring offers an alternative to adversarial relationships and hard times. Too often, economic and other business factors pit people against each other. A work group may see themselves as competing for scarce resources. A company may be conducting layoffs or cutting pay and benefits. When offered at the workplace, the wins engendered through Wellness Mentoring can counterbalance the negative and divisive consequences of some business practices.

👍 Wellness Mentoring connects people who might not otherwise meet. When employees are paired for mutual support, matches can be organized around compatible schedules or similarities in behavior goals. These Wellness Mentoring match-ups can mix employees of various job functions, seniority and power. This enhances cross-functional communication, fosters an appreciation of other work groups and helps employees feel connected with the corporate identity.

👍 Wellness Mentoring puts a human face on business. Some businesses sell themselves short by focusing exclusively on product and profit without seeing the value of their people. In such a climate, an employee is likely to be viewed by shareholders and senior managers as a cost of doing business rather than a human asset. In contrast, where people examine their wellness goals and share them with others, they become a unique contributor and valued in the workplace.

👍 Wellness Mentoring aligns human and economic interests. This is a major achievement of a healthy corporate culture. Personal goals and work goals are often compatible, and also complementary. As we saw with health behavior and illness, achieving wellness goals provides less costly, more productive and more dependable employees.

Wellness Mentoring enhances social capital in a multitude of ways. However, there are limits to the impact of Wellness Mentoring in that it does not directly address some of the structural factors that may be undermining social relationships. For example, it may be that organizational leaders are not focused on creating a good work atmosphere, or, as is more likely the case, they do not know how to effectively address their work climate.

If you are passionate about doing more to address social capital at your worksite, you can learn more about the subject by taking the training at www.healthyworkclimate.com. And you can join with a peer to consider how you might engage your leaders in the value of addressing social capital in the workplace.

Bowling Together

Do we have enough opportunities for experiencing kindness and connection? Robert Putnam, author of *Bowling Alone,* conducted an extensive analysis of research on this question and found a recent decline of more than 20 percent in many aspects of social relations. Professor Putnam found that we used to belong to clubs, know our neighbors, engage in community politics, volunteer, eat with family members and host dinner parties. Such social activities have become increasingly rare. The overall trend was summed up in the demise of social bowling throughout America. Whereas we used to bowl in leagues, we now tend to bowl alone.

Professor Putnam looks at the benefits of social relationships in terms of broad societal outcomes. He says that social bonds are the most powerful predictor of life satisfaction. For example, getting married is the equivalent in terms of happiness of quadrupling your income, and attending a club meeting regularly is the equivalent of doubling your income.

In contrast, the loss of social bonds is revealed in lower educational performance and more teen pregnancy, child suicide, low birth weight and prenatal mortality. The quality of social relationships is a strong predictor of crime rates and other measures of neighborhood quality of life. Positive wellness-oriented relationships available through Wellness Mentoring are a bridge from negative influences of social groups. For example, this approach would turn around college alcohol abuse and street gang violence.

Professor Putnam calls for new social mechanisms that respond to modern times. He points out that permanent employment is largely a relic of the past. Traditional family relationships are no longer the norm. Suburban sprawl means that people tend to work, shop and live in different areas. With this shift in lifestyle, the likelihood of chance meetings with friends is diminished.

Leisure-time activities have changed, with many technologies such as TV and the Internet offering a substitute for face-to-face interaction. Even architecture is playing a role as fewer homes are built with front porches.

Wellness Mentoring offers a mechanism for rebuilding social bonds in modern times. The one-to-one connection can adapt to modern work and living arrangements. A mix of in-person conversations supported by telephone and email communication fits today's needs well. Because traditional family roles and work ties have broken down, Wellness Mentoring offers a new way to build caring relationships and an additional reason to connect with peers. It doesn't rely on traditional family configurations or old-style hierarchical decision-making structures. With Wellness Mentoring we are not managing or manipulating people. This is not a way to get others to do what we think they should do. Instead, we are empowering people to help one another as equals – as peers.

Wellness Mentoring adds modern "oomph" to social relationships. It offers a format and content for solid helping relationships. Many of us have lost the art of connecting. We have been "bowling alone" for so long that we feel odd spending time with others. We also feel awkward because relationships have been devalued and manipulated. Tupperware parties and network marketing have turned many friendships into a commercial enterprise. Wellness Mentoring reclaims helping for the sake of helping. It is commercial-free. It is a healthy way to "bowl" together.

Creating Opportunities for Wellness Mentoring

As we stated in the *Call to Action*, a primary purpose of *Not Alone* is to make peer support less threatening, more effective and more available. The idea of learning to give and receive effective peer support is a new idea that goes beyond the typical self-help approach. Wellness Mentoring is many notches up from the more typical chance or informal peer support that most of us have experienced. Like any new idea, you will need to reach out and explain to others how Wellness Mentoring works. You should soon have some successful experiences to share. Real-life stories tend to be persuasive. In addition, I recommend that you offer your peers a copy of this book.

I believe that *Not Alone* can play an important role in enhancing your wellness, and the wellness of the people in your life. I also believe that this approach to powerful peer support can help bring about the wellness revolution that is so urgently needed to ensure the well being of individuals and the planet. Your love and support can be instrumental in making this happen. You can spread the word by sharing your Wellness Mentoring stories.

Please reach out to your peers when you see them struggling with personal change. Lend them your copy of this book and encourage them to get support. Show a peer how to support you when you need it. I also hope that you will recommend *Not Alone* to people in workplaces, health care settings and community groups. Consider the following uses:

In a worksite, *Not Alone* could be:

👆 Given as a follow-up incentive for taking a health risk appraisal, attending a wellness seminar or participating in a support group.

- ♨ Part of a wellness buddy initiative in which employees voluntarily pair-up for mutual support in lowering health risks.

- ♨ Offered as a holiday gift for a healthier New Year.

- ♨ Provided to new employees as part of the company orientation.

- ♨ Incorporated into a teamwork and morale-building initiative.

- ♨ Sent out accompanying information about corporate health benefits.

- ♨ Incorporated into peer support training for members of a wellness committee or safety team.

- ♨ Integrated into the employee assistance program or corporate health center protocols.

In health care settings and with private or public health insurance providers, *Not Alone* could be:

- ♨ Distributed to a beneficiary's family members or house-mates as part of their chronic care treatment or as a follow-up to treatment for lifestyle-related illnesses.

- ♨ Incorporated into the continuing education of health professionals to increase their awareness of the vital role peers play in supporting health behavior changes.

- ♨ Incorporated into a wellness buddy program in which patients assist one another with their wellness goals.

- ♨ Added to the lending library.

❧ Incorporated into the welcome packet for new members and plan participants.

❧ Sent to plan participants as part of a health and wellness education initiative.

In a school, community group or religious organization, *Not Alone* could be:

❧ Added to the lending library.

❧ Incorporated into the orientation as a way for new members to develop friendships.

❧ Included in a lecture or sermon on health and the importance of human connections.

❧ Offered as a follow-up to health counseling and support groups.

❧ Incorporated into a wellness buddy program in which members or students assist one another with wellness goals.

Looking to the Future

Keep your Wellness Mentoring skills fresh. Review the book and revisit the many questions and assignments here. You'll be surprised how your interpretation of our recommendations and your perspectives about effective peer support will evolve over time.

The book draws on many years of research, personal experience and wisdom offered by many health and wellness professionals. The Recommended Books list at the end of this book features ideas that may be particularly helpful in reinforcing key Wellness Mentoring ideas and in broadening your perspectives on wellness and helping relationships.

You can learn a great deal from others who are engaged in *Not Alone*. To this end we have created a website at www.wellnessmentor.net. With your input, this site offers examples of best practices, video testimonials, online discussion boards and training courses. Use the website to further enhance your skills and consider participating in continuing education opportunities offered at the annual National Wellness Conference (see www.nationalwellness.org). I look forward to seeing you there.

Wellness Mentoring Stories

- In Michigan, the City of Kalamazoo's wellness council was seeking to increase the capacity of citizens to get involved in supporting each other so they set up a training initiative that focused on peer support. Participants attended follow-up meetings and plugged into a website designed to support the initiative. More than 500 participants joined together for the effort that bridged economic, religious and business boundaries.

- The University of Vermont hoped that undergrads would form their early college friendships around healthy behaviors. A course was created that incorporated Wellness Mentoring skills into the curriculum. Students were organized into groups of three, and 20 minutes of weekly course time was set aside to discuss wellness goals and their peer support. Students submitted a log of their efforts and a final report on their progress.

- Union Pacific Railroad wanted to create a wellness culture throughout its multi-state network. They incorporated Wellness Mentoring lessons into training for safety captains. Participants were encouraged to serve as wellness mentors, and a referral system was set up fo employees seeking assistance with health behavior change.

- A state school system incorporated Wellness Mentoring skills into its health risk appraisal (HRA). Employees checked a box at the end of their online HRA to indicate their desire to be matched with Wellness Coaches. A website assisted school employees in working with their Wellness Coaches to lower health risks.

Bringing on the Wellness Revolution Checklist

The following checklist helps determine how you might continue to work with *Not Alone*. Consider these approaches to bringing on the wellness revolution:

☐ I promote wellness locally and nationally.

☐ I find ways to use social connections to promote healing.

☐ I find ways to use social capital for business outcomes.

☐ I find ways to help my community and society through enhanced human connections.

☐ I find ways to promote Wellness Mentoring in workplaces, groups and organizations.

☐ I join with others in learning more about and improving upon the Wellness Mentoring concept.

☐ I am looking for ways to improve upon and advance the Wellness Mentoring concept.

☐ I share success stories about how Wellness Mentoring made it possible to help others and to achieve my wellness goals.

Recommended Books

Aldana, S.G. (2005). *The Culprit & the Cure.* **Mapleton, UT: Maple Mountain Press.**

Dr. Aldana has organized the U.S. evidence linking health to health behavior. The book explains the tragic health consequences of a population that is trending toward unhealthy behaviors. It offers guidance useful for examining personal practices and for setting behavior change goals.

Allen, R. F. & Linde, S. (1981). *Lifegain.* **Second Edition. Burlington, VT: Human Resources Institute Press.**

Lifegain provides an overview of the wellness concept and the role of culture in shaping health behavior. Included are a life expectancy test, a cultural assessment, and action plans for physical fitness, smoking cessation, healthy eating, weight management, alcohol use, accident prevention, stress management and healthy relationships. The final chapter offers an outline for designing a health promotion program at a worksite or for an entire community.

Ardell, D. B. (2007). *Under the Influence of a Wellness Lifestyle.* **Duluth, MN: Whole Person Associates.**

Dr. Ardell is best known for his wit and wisdom in explaining how the wellness approach differs from the traditional approach to health and illness. This book explains how we would all benefit from adopting wellness lifestyles. *Under the Influence* features 69 tips for aging healthfully, with panache and the highest possible quality of life. Dr. Ardell's monthly and weekly insights are also available in *The Ardell Wellness Report* at www.seekwellness.com/wellness.

Bandura, A. (1976). *Social Learning Theory.* **Englewood Cliffs, NJ: Prentice-Hall.**

Albert Bandura is best known for his research on modeling behavior. This book includes a discussion of the role of modeling in shaping behavior.

Cohen D. & Prusak, L. (2001). *In Good Company.* **Boston, MA: Harvard Business School Press.**

Good social relationships make for good business. These authors have compiled extensive evidence for how social bonds, referred to as social capital, not only increase teamwork, but are essential to good customer relations and even to the vitality of entire industries. They show how the breakdown of social capital leads to complications such as the need for increased paperwork and litigation.

Harris, T. A. (1973). *I'm OK - You're OK.* **New York: Avon Books.**

James, M. & Jongeward, D. (1996). *Born to Win.* **Reading, MA: Addison-Wesley.**

These two books explain Transactional Analysis, a method of examining the hidden messages in our conversations with others. For example, there is a tendency for conversations about lifestyle to be experienced as between a parent and a child. Do we come across as adults, children or parents? Wellness Mentors can use Transactional Analysis to untangle confusing conversations. Generally speaking, the mentor will want to transform the conversation so that everyone feels like an adult.

Huang, C. A. & Lynch, J. (1995). *Mentoring: The Tao of Giving and Receiving Wisdom.* **San Francisco: HarperCollins.**

This book offers a Taoist philosophy perspective on mentoring. A short list of words such as *trustfulness* and *decisiveness* are used to discuss the mentoring process.

Leutzinger, J. & Harris, J. (2006). *How & Why People Change Health Behavior.* **Omaha, NE: Health Improvement Solutions.**
This book shares health behavior change success stories. These stories are inspiring and offer insight into the many ways people give and get help with lifestyle change.

Lipman, D. (1995). *The Storytelling Coach.* **Little Rock, AR: August House.**
This book goes beyond teaching readers how to help people tell stories. *The Storytelling Coach* provides important principles for supporting others.

Marlatt, G. A. & Gordon, J. R. (2005). *Relapse Prevention.* **New York: Guilford Press.**
This book provides an extensive review of the research on relapse and offers recommendations for helping people to keep their lifestyle change efforts on track.

Maslow, A. H. (1968). *Toward a Psychology of Being.* **Second Edition. New York: D. Van Nostrand Company.**
This book tells important truths about human potential and motivation. Maslow explains the hierarchy of human needs. The hierarchy of motivation begins with basic survival. At the other end of his continuum is a vision of full mental health, called self-actualization. Using Maslow's framework, we can begin to understand individual values and beliefs. We can use this knowledge to help people better achieve their full potential.

Ornish, D. (1998). *Love & Survival.* **New York: Harper Collins.**

Dr. Ornish assembles the massive evidence that our relationships hold the key to whether we get sick, when we die and how fast we recover from illness. The book discusses a broad range of studies that show that the quality of our communities, our participation in those communities and how we relate to each other plays a powerful role in health that is at least as important as other risk factors such as smoking and inactivity.

Ornish, D. (1990). *Dr. Dean Ornish's Program for Reversing Heart Disease.* **New York: Random House.**

Dr. Ornish has been brilliant at proving to a skeptical medical community that adopting a healthy lifestyle can reverse heart disease. Participants in Ornish's programs maintain their behaviors through support groups and by distancing themselves from common, but unhealthy, cultural norms. Although few people have the resources to attend Ornish's intensive program, we can learn a lot from the achievements of program participants.

Ornstein, R. & Sobel, D. (1989). *Healthy Pleasures.* **Reading, MA: Addison-Wesley.**

Ornstein and Sobel provide compelling evidence that nearly everything that people naturally like to do is good for them. Sex, touching, eating, smelling, laughing, seeing things of beauty all reduce our risk of getting sick and help us to a speedy recovery. The authors believe that we pay too much attention to telling people what is risky and not enough attention to what is fun and pleasurable. They give ample justification for putting pleasure back into life. The authors also remind their readers about life's simple pleasures.

Prochaska, J. O., Norcross, J. C. & DiClemente, C. C. (1994).
Changing for Good. **New York: William Morrow and Company.**

It is normal to view lifestyle change as an event rather than as a
process. For example, someone might say, "I quit smoking on
July 1, 1996." The authors of *Changing for Good* have found that
it is far more helpful to view change as an ongoing process. The
primary advantage of working with a process is that it lowers
failure rates. In addition, treating lifestyle change as a process
makes it possible to work with people who either are not ready
to act or are having difficulty sustaining new lifestyle practices.
The authors have identified six stages (discussed in this book in
chapter 2) that are common to lifestyle change. They explain how
we can work the six-stage process to achieve lasting results.

Putnam, J.D. (2000). *Bowling Alone.* **New York: Simon &
Schuster.**

Professor Putnam offers an in-depth look at how social relationships
have ebbed and flowed in American life. He points out that we have
lost approximately a quarter of our positive social interaction in our
homes, at work and in our community. He shows how these trends
adversely affect communities, families, democracy, health, business
activity and overall quality of life. Robert Putnam examines
hundreds of studies that show the negative impact of current
trends. He offers guidance in reversing the current breakdown.

Travis, J.W. & Ryan, R.S. (2004). *Wellness Workbook.* **Third
Edition. Berkeley, CA: Celestial Arts.**

Wellness is more than just not being sick. This book broadens
and deepens our wellness vision with an examination of the many
facets of wellness. The authors see wellness as a process of discov-
ery and growth, and when reading the *Wellness Workbook* you can't
help but discover new and relatively unexplored facets of your
own life. This book touches and examines all aspects of the human experience with subjects as diverse as how we communicate,
have sex, enjoy music and approach spirituality.

Glossary

Barriers to Change — Successful behavior change frequently requires resources such as time, equipment, mental capacity and the cooperation of others. Lack of needed resources makes it difficult to modify behavior and constitutes barriers to change. Wellness Mentors assist their peers to cope with, overcome and eliminate barriers to change.

Cultural Climate — A sense of community, a shared vision and a positive outlook are social environmental factors that enhance the capacity of individuals and organizations to grow. A sense of community provides for trust and openness. A shared vision enables people to be inspired by a common direction. A positive outlook makes it possible to use individual and collective strengths in meeting challenges. Together, these factors constitute the level of cultural climate that is present at work, at home or in the community. Peer support is frequently directed at limiting exposure to unhealthy social climates and increasing exposure to settings with strong senses of community, shared visions and positive outlooks.

Cultural Norms — The accepted and expected behavior of a culture are its norms. Sometimes such behaviors are referred to as "the way we do things around here." People are most likely to be aware of norms when they are new to a culture and are wondering how they are expected to behave. Wellness Mentors help determine if norms at home, work and in the community support desired healthy behavior. Goals could be set for reducing contact with subcultures that have unsupportive norms. Wellness Mentors also identify groups that have strong norms for desired health behavior. For example, someone seeking to be physically active is likely to benefit from becoming a member of a walking group.

Cultural Touch Points — Subcultures and the broader society influence behavior through 10 broad and overlapping mechanisms called touch points. They are (1) rewards, (2) confrontation, (3) modeling, (4) recruitment and selection, (5) orientation, (6) training, (7) communication including what is talked about and measured, (8) relationship development including how people form teams and friendships, (9) rites, rituals and symbols including holidays, events and important stories, and (10) resource commitment including how time and money are spent. Wellness Mentors examine these touch points to determine how social influences support or fail to support behavior change goals. Mentors work with their peers to find or create subcultures that more fully support desired behavior.

Extrinsic Rewards — Peers, groups and society reinforce behavior through social recognition, benefits, incentives or other forms of payment. These rewards are known as extrinsic in that they are provided by others. Prizes, praise, job promotion and salaries are examples of extrinsic rewards. Wellness Mentors provide praise and other extrinsic rewards for progress toward health behavior change. Wellness Mentors may also be helpful in seeking out the extrinsic rewards that may be available for achieving healthy lifestyle goals.

Intrinsic Rewards — Healthy behaviors have varied benefits to the changer. An intrinsic reward is a benefit that directly results from behavior change, for example, feeling more energetic after becoming more fit. An ex-smoker gets fewer colds, a longer life expectancy, improved athletic performance and a reduced risk of becoming impotent (for men). This is over and above the new freedom and lowered expense of breaking free of smoking addiction. Wellness Mentors can assist in identifying the many positive rewards that are the direct result of the new health behavior.

Peers — Coworkers, spouses, housemates, friends, neighbors and co-participants in rehabilitation, health or wellness programs have interests and experiences in common. Peers have similar standing and power. Peers are the people in our groups, workplaces and communities that we view as equals. By becoming Wellness Mentors, our peers can play important roles in helping us to achieve personal goals.

Relapse — People often revert back to previous and undesired practices when attempting to change unhealthy habits. These setbacks are called relapses. Peers help limit relapses by developing strategies for coping with and avoiding difficult situations. When relapse occurs, Wellness Mentors assist with getting back on track, limiting self-doubt and guilt and adjusting change tactics.

Role Model — It's likely that someone achieved the same behavior change goal you seek under very similar circumstances. A person who has achieved such a change could become a role model if he is willing to tell his story. A lot can be learned from such success experiences. They are proof that change is possible and desirable. Role models can explain their experience including what worked and what did not work. A Wellness Mentor does not need to be the role model. She can help find and interview potential role models.

Stages of Behavior Change — Successful behavior change tends to follow a six-step progression that is called stages of behavior change. The first stage is devoted to developing the reasons for making the change. Stage two involves picking a time for making the change. The third stage involves selecting the strategies for making the change. Stage four is the action stage when behavior begins to change. Stage five is focused on keeping the new behavior going. The final or sixth stage is a time when the new desired behavior is firmly in place and the person is ready to move on to other goals. Wellness Mentors can help their peers to determine where they are in the change process so that appropriate goals and tasks can be set. Mentors can also celebrate success along the way and use the stages of behavior change to reestablish progress during any relapse.

Wellness — People can consciously choose to live in ways that maximize their health, quality of life and personal performance. Personal wellness is multi-dimensional and holistic, encompassing mental and physical well being as well as a person's relationships with others and nature. Wellness mentors assist in setting personally satisfying wellness goals that are both positive and affirming.

Wellness Buddies — Sometimes peers partner up to achieve wellness goals. Wellness buddies are friends, family and coworkers who achieve goals together. An example of wellness buddies would be two friends who get together for a morning walk to achieve physical activity goals. New relationships are sometimes formed specifically for companionship in taking on a wellness goal. Such wellness buddy relationships may form in support groups, at health seminars, in rehabilitation programs and at health clubs. A wellness mentor could be a wellness buddy. Often, however, mentors assist in finding another peer interested in becoming a wellness buddy.

Wellness Mentoring — Listening and offering words of encouragement are typical forms of support given by friends, family and coworkers to achieve healthy habits. Wellness Mentors go beyond such assistance by strategically focusing on a full range of lifestyle change support including help with setting goals, eliminating barriers to change, identifying role models, locating supportive environments, working through relapse and celebrating success. Follow-through is another distinctive feature of Wellness Mentoring. The mentor meets regularly with her peer to keep behavior change moving forward.

References

A Call to Action

Allen, J. (1984). Correlates of Success in Lifestyle Change Efforts. Paper presented at the 92nd annual meeting of the American Psychological Association, Toronto, Canada.

Allen, J. (2001). Building supportive cultural environments. In *Health Promotion in the Workplace,* Michael P. O'Donnell, editor, Third Edition, Delmar Publishers, Inc., Albany, New York, pp. 202-217.

Franklin, B. (1998). *The Autobiography of Benjamin Franklin.* New York: Wordsworth Editions.

Twain, M. (1993). *The Adventures of Huckleberry Finn.* New York: Modern Library.

Allen, R. F. & Allen, J. (1983). Lifegain: A new way of helping young people to create positive health-supporting cultures. *New Designs for Youth Development,* 4:5, pp. 21-28.

Bandura, A. (1977). *Social Learning Theory.* Englewood Cliffs, NJ: Prentice-Hall.

Prochaska, J.O., Norcross, J.C., & DiClemente, C.C. (1994). *Changing for Good: A revolutionary six-stage program for overcoming bad habits and moving your life positively forward.* New York: William Morrow and Company.

Allen, J. (2002). The role of mentoring in health promotion. *The Art of Health Promotion.* March/April, 6:4; 1-12.

Travis, J.W. & Ryan, R.S. (2004). *Wellness Workbook: How to Achieve Enduring Health and Vitality.* Third Edition. Berkley, California: Celestial Arts.

Setting Goals

Prochaska, J. O., Norcross, J. C. & DiClemente, C. C. (1994). *Changing for Good.* New York: William Morrow and Company.

Identifying Role Models

Jonas, S. (1996). *The Essential Triathlete.* New York: The Lyons Press.

Working through Relapse

Seligman, M.E.P. (1998). *Learned Optimism.* New York: Pocket Books.

Celebrating Success

Prochaska, J. O., Norcross, J. C. & DiClemente, C. C. (1994). *Changing for Good.* New York: William Morrow and Company.

Life Expectancy Test reprinted with permission from Allen, R. F. & Linde, S. (1981). *Lifegain: A Culture-Based Approach to Positive Health.* Second Edition. Burlington, VT: Human Resources Institute Press, pp. 19-20.

Bringing on the Wellness Revolution

Consumer Reports on Health. August 2006, Vol. 18, Number 8, p. 5.

Steve G. Aldana (2005). *The Culprit & the Cure: Why Lifestyle Is the Culprit Behind America's Poor Health and How Transforming that Lifestyle Can Be the Cure.* Mapleton, UT: Maple Mountain Press. Available from Wellness Councils of America at www.welcoa.org.

Ornish, Dean (1997). *Love & Survival: The Scientific Basis for the Healing Power of Intimacy.* New York, Harper Collins.

Depner, C.E. & Ingersoll-Dayton (1988). "Supportive relationships in later life." *Psychology and Aging,* 3:348-57 as cited in Dean Ornish (1997). *Love & Survival: The Scientific Basis for the Healing Power of Intimacy.* New York, Harper Collins, p. 29.

Cohen, D. & Prusak, L. (2001). *In Good Company: How Social Capital Makes Organizations Work.* Boston: Harvard Business School Press.

Putnam, R.D. (2000). *Bowling Alone: The Collapse and Revival of American Community.* New York: Simon & Schuster.

Quick Order Form

Fax orders: 802-862-6389

Telephone orders: Call 800-800-3004 in the U.S. or 802-862-8855

Email orders: Info@healthyculture.com

Postal orders: Healthyculture.com, 151 Dunder Road, Burlington, Vermont, 05401 USA

Number of Books _____

Cost of 1st book $19.95.

Cost of 2nd book $9.95. Call for bulk order pricing.

Please add 8% sales tax for books shipped to a Vermont address.

Please add $5 for first book shipped by air within the U.S. and $2 for each additional book.

Please add $9 for first book shipped outside the U.S and $5 for each additional international order.

Name

Address

Telephone

Email

We gladly accept checks in U.S. funds payable to the Human Resources Institute, LLC

To pay by MasterCard or VISA

Card Number _____

Expiration date _____

Billing address if other than shipping address